# WE'RE THE GIRLS

# WE'RE THE GIRLS

## AND OTHER SONGS, STORIES AND MONOLOGUES BY

# Clare Summerskill

### ILLUSTRATED BY

### Kate Charlesworth

Diana Publishing

First published 2008 by Diana Publishing,
58 St Albans Crescent, London N22 5NB

ISBN 978-0-9558308-0-8

Cover illustration by Kate Charlesworth
Cover design by Sarah Wood
Typeset by Helen Sandler
Printed and bound in the UK by Biddles

www.claresummerskill.co.uk

# CONTENTS

# FOREWORD

In the shows that I have been touring to theatres around the country, I have written and performed monologues portraying different women from the lesbian community. They are, I suppose, stereotypes in one sense, but in another way they are unique individuals who tell us about their own lives and loves from their own particular perspective.

Sometimes people say that there is no such thing as a lesbian community – and that is true in so much as we live in a predominantly straight world – but we as lesbians do have our own ways, our own lifestyles and our own history and I hope that these characters, as well as the stories and songs in this book, will go some way to celebrating that wonderful difference.

My thanks go to Kate Charlesworth who has brought her unique talent to this book by providing what I believe are perfect illustrations of the women I have written about. I would also like to thank Helen Sandler for all her work in helping me to produce this book.

*Clare Summerskill*

# WE'RE THE GIRLS

CHORUS:

We're the girls your mother should have warned you about.
We may appear quite harmless but we're always looking out
For a certain sort of woman who may never once suspect
The lust we feel for her is not politically correct.
And even if she says she's straight, there's always room for
    doubt,
And her mother should have warned her there are girls like us
    about.

You may express alarm at my condition
But from a very early age I learned to drool.
I remember I was seven and I thought I'd gone to heaven
When Miss Knight said I was bright
And that she'd coach me after school.

Teenage girls are warned about the danger
Of mysterious men who steal their hearts away,
But you couldn't call Miss Middleton a stranger
And I'd fantasise in history class
About her every day.

(CHORUS)

In later years I made my way to college
And on a tutor I developed quite a crush.
As I tried to give my view on how Communism grew,
My legs would turn to jelly and my face would start to flush.

9

I wish I didn't fancy my new doctor.
I was scared to go for my cervical smear.
As I lay down on the couch, I got ready to cry ouch,
But she touched me oh so gently – now I've booked one twice
    a year.

(CHORUS)

Well, now I know the cause of my obsession,
I'm fully out and happy that I'm gay,
But let me make a very small confession:
Although I have a lover, there are times that I could stray.

There's a programme that I like called *Supernanny*
Where this woman teaches calm authority.
I go funny in my tummy, perhaps I'm looking for a mummy,
But I'd gladly misbehave if she would take control of me.

(CHORUS)

## LESBIAN SHOPKEEPER

Can I help you, Madam? You'd like a lesbian, would you? For yourself or for a friend? ... For yourself. That shouldn't be a problem, we've a lot in stock at the moment, they seem to be all the rage. I'm sure we'll be able to find you someone suitable, then we'll draw up a contract and voilà!

The contract? Oh it's standard procedure, Madam. All you have to do is sign a little form saying that the relationship with the lovely lesbian lady that I find for you will last forever. No, Madam, of course it doesn't matter if you split up with her at a later date, it's just something lesbians tell each other when they first meet. It's purely a formality. Just something you say. Yes, even if you don't mean it. I sense Madam's a first-time buyer, am I correct? Yes, I thought so!

Now, had Madam any particular kind of lesbian in mind?

"Late twenties, good sense of humour..." I'm assuming then that Madam hasn't seen our latest catalogue? No? Well, you see, it's just that that sort of description is, how shall I put it? ... A little vague.

May I make a suggestion? I'll go through some types and then Madam can stop me when she hears one that takes her fancy. Righty ho!

Now, would Madam be looking for a butch or a femme? A top or a bottom? A dominant or submissive? A butch with femme rising? (Very popular at the moment!) Or possibly a controlling femme. (On second thoughts, I wouldn't recommend that for a first-time buyer.) Now a butch bottom might be more to Madam's taste, if Madam will pardon the expression.

Yes, Madam, it *is* far more complicated than most people assume. But worth all the trouble in the end, I think you'll agree.

Now, dress styles. Some of these are new this season and some go back quite a few years but still prove popular with the ladies. We can offer you: denim, grunge, lipstick lesbian, New Age... Stop me if something jumps out at you... Leather, skinhead, seventies, Generation X... No? Nothing there?

Let's move on then to lifestyles. Vegetarian woolly jumper, brown bread lesbian. Cat-loving, child replacement lesbian. Homeopathic up a shamanic mountain lesbian. Or there's always your basic dyke-riding lesbian. Sorry, that's a typing error, it should read "bike-riding" lesbian...

Anything there? No? Well, moving swiftly on: drug or alcohol addiction? I'm sorry, I can't just take "No" as a reply, it's an either/or question. This is a lesbian shop after all.

Oh dear, Madam seems quite overwhelmed! Look, how about I leave you to look over this questionnaire and then you just tick what interests you and from that I'll find your perfect partner and you can take her home today complete with guarantee. The guarantee? Two weeks. Yes, I appreciate it might not seem that long, but believe me, Madam, I have known lesbians meet, fall in love, move in with each other, get a mortgage, fall out of love, go to couple therapy, arrange custody of the cat and finally split up, all within the space of forty-eight hours. So you see, two weeks is a little over-optimistic, if anything.

Is there really nothing here that takes your fancy? What? *I* do? Well, yes, I am single and yes, I am free after work, but why wait till then? Come through. It'll be a pleasure serving you!

## ANGE: A BIG SOFTY

*Ange's voice is quite a low one, and her accent is from the East End of London.*

Hello there. My name's Angela but everyone calls me "Ange". I'm a publican and I do prefer that word to the other one, "landlady". I run a small lesbian establishment with gay men welcome as guests on the outskirts of the city of Oxford. When I took it over the pub was called "The Flying Cock" but I thought some of the girls might think twice about coming to a place with a name like that, so I changed it to "Ellen's". I did send her an invite for the opening. I'm not backward in coming forward, me. Thought she might drop by, you know, if she was free. 'Cos we had it so everyone got their first drink on the house and then there was nibbles as well so I hoped she might be tempted but... well she didn't show. I know she's a busy woman but if you don't ask you don't get, do you? That's what I say.

So yes, I run my own pub and I've seen quite a lot of goings-on with the girls that frequent my place. But I'm always the one they come to when they're having problems. And I know I might seem a bit frightening to you what with my leather trousers and my tattoos... and before you ask, no, I'm not going to show you the ones you can't already see. But you won't find no body-piercings on me. 'Cos I think that's a bit weird, I do. Tattoos, yes. But self-mutilation, no thank you! But like I was saying, deep down, me, I'm just a big softy, I am.

Like when it comes to young lesbians who've maybe split up with their girlfriends and need a shoulder to cry on... or a place to stay for the night. And yes, I have been known to let a girl stay in my flat, if she's got troubles and the like. 'Cos it's right

above the pub, you see. And there's only me up there rattling around – oh, and of course my cats. Lady and Lulu. Mustn't forget them. They're my princesses, and I spoil them rotten. I let them sleep on the bed and everything. And if I'm ever with anyone who maybe gets a little jealous of the attention I give to my cats and perhaps they might say, "Ange, sometimes I think you prefer your cats to me!" And I'll say, "Well, as a matter of fact, Bev, or Jenny or whoever the particular girl might be... truth be told, I do!" How I see it is that girlfriends come and go, but cats stay with you forever (unless of course they get run over, heaven forbid).

But I do like being my own boss. Oh yeah. You see, I used to be a prison officer. Now, I don't always tell people that, 'cos there's certain girls out there who... well, let's just say they might get ideas in their heads about what they could get up to with me. I'm being quite serious here. It has happened. A certain girlfriend liked me to put the uniform on out of hours, shall we say. But as I said to the girl at the time, "I'm not into all that." Sexy stuff, yes, pervy stuff, no thank you!

But this job suits me much better than the prison service did. And of course there's a whole range of people that you meet. All walks of life. We had a chiropodist come in last weekend. Yeah.

But it's hard work, I can tell you. I didn't get a holiday at all this year. Except that long weekend I went down to Eastbourne. You know? The tennis tournament? I'm a Kournikova fan myself. Yeah. Don't get me wrong, I mean I respect Martina, Amelie, Conchita, but in the bedroom department, if I had to choose, well, Anna would be the girl for me. I've got her poster upstairs in my room. Signed. I go to sleep looking at that. Very nice definition. But I'll tell you something. If Anna was staying and *she* got a bit uppity about, say, the cat hairs on the bed, I'd say, "Listen, darling. I appreciate that you're an internationally renowned sportswoman and all that but right now, love, I think you'll find that you're in *my* flat and here we do things *my* way, all right?"

And then maybe she'd look somewhat surprised at my harsh words and go a bit teary-eyed and that and I'd probably end up by saying, "Oh, all right then, just this once – since, to be honest, it's probably only likely to be the one night – I'll close the door and leave the cats in the corridor for the night."

'Cos that's me all over. I'm just a big softy, I am!

# MAGDELINA

*Magdelina has a west coast American accent.*

Welcome to each and every one of you wonderful women and your beautiful individual energies and auras. Welcome to this year's Women's Festival and Camp Retreat or, as it has become known over the years, Woofercera.

For those of you who don't know me, my name is Magdelina. And to kick off with some good news, I'd like to tell you all that I am currently single! Whoop! Thank you! Yes, I have finished with Rose and we are now incommunicado on account of the litigation procedure that she is bringing against me, suing me for half the profits from the last ten years of WFCR – which, even though I totally organised and bankrolled it, she now says that she did half the work for. Yeah, right! And I can see a few of you shaking your heads in disbelief, because I'm sure you remember all too well that she spent most of her time here last year totally inebriated on dandelion and nettle wine which she drank in the woods with her so-called "friend", Rebecca, the reiki workshop leader with whom she is now cohabiting.

So, thank you for your love and concern and yes, I can feel it coming across the field right now and up onto the stage, but I am confident that I will succeed in this particular life challenge and be totally protected from harm, not only by the white light which surrounds us all, but also by my good friend and ex-lover, Anna, who is an extremely high-profile lawyer and who will be representing me in court next month.

So, if any of you want to make a pass at me, do feel free! I can safely say that I have finished the grieving process and am ready for a new experience.

So, as you all know, the theme to this year's WFCR is Back to

Nature – and on that note, I have to mention bathroom facilities. After last year's problems with women digging so many individual holes around the campsite and the subsequent collapse of many areas after heavy rainfall, I am pleased to announce that we now have Portaloos for the very first time. We are, however, going to have to charge you a very small amount each time you wish to use them, but I know you will believe me when I say that this year we have really tried to keep costs low in every area in camp.

Now, just a quick word on the wonderful workshops we have in store for you this year – and please remember that if you don't have cash with you, you can pay your workshop leader direct with all major credit cards.

Last year many of you signed up for the "Feel the Fear and Do It Even if You Don't Feel Like Doing It" workshops and we are delighted to have Tanya Green back with us, albeit on crutches this time, I'm sorry to say, on account of a little sky-diving accident that she had recently. But she's back anyway and she'll be running a course with a slightly different theme this year called "Feel the Fear and Do Something that Perhaps Isn't Quite So Dangerous".

Amy Fowler over there will be presenting a demonstration for first-timers here. What's it called, Amy? "Putting Up Tents Doesn't Have To Be". Doesn't have to be what? Tense? I don't get it, Amy, and if I don't, believe me, no-one else will.

And now, if you're one of those people, like me, who've always thought that shamanism was a load of old nonsense, then let me tell you that I have seriously changed my mind on that subject after meeting our new shamanic drum and dance co-ordinator, the very beautiful Liz, who is – and I hope I don't embarrass her by saying this – a very sexually vibrant person whom I would dearly love to get to know on a more intimate basis, if you know what I mean, Liz.

Later this evening, Liz will be running "The Endless Dance of the Universe". But I do have to say, Liz, that "Endless" it might well be called but there will still have to be a cut-off point at eleven p.m. so as not to disturb the other campers with all that racket. OK, honey?

And finally, I'm delighted to say that we have many women signed up for our Women and Harmony Groups. The magic of music is in us all, so let yourself go and sing, play and dance your way to release the freedom of your soul. But please do remember that the emphasis here *is* on harmony and that if you're someone who perhaps sings a little out of tune, it can really be annoying for the others, so if you still feel the need to sing, perhaps you could just kind of do it real quietly, or even mime. That would be so much better.

OK, that's all from me. And don't forget that my door is always open – or perhaps I should say, my tent flaps! So, any time you want to talk to me or just have a little cuddle, do drop by, unless of course the lovely shamanic Liz is already in with me, in which case, Please Do Not Disturb!

# BETTY

*Betty has a strong West Country accent.*

Has the show started already? The lesbian entertainment? Have I missed it? Oh bugger! But I am in the right place, aren't I? I can tell. You see, my daughter, Alison, she's like you girls. Well, a bit like some of you anyway. She's of your "way of being", shall we say? Yeah. Now, do you mind if I just sit down a minute? Take the weight off my feet.

Oh, that's better! I've been doing some shopping. It's exhausting, isn't it?

See, I'm up in London cat-sitting for my daughter, the one that's like you. She's got a little place round the corner and she's gone on holiday with her girlfriend. Gone on a lesbian cruise, she has. That's what she called it. But she says, "Mum, it's not what you think. It's just like any normal cruise ship, but women only." So that's nice, isn't it? She's having a break... while I'm having her kit-kat!

Don't mind me. That's just my sense of humour.

So, I saw the poster for this show outside and I thought I'd come and see this lesbian entertainment – 'cos they don't have many shows like this where I live in Barnstaple – and perhaps I'd meet some other girls like my Alison.

Well, obviously it was a little bit of a surprise when she first told me. I'd be lying if I said it wasn't. But then, looking back over her childhood and that, a lot of things sort of fell into place. Like how she cried for weeks when her friend Linda Hodges moved to Bedford. And how she was always a bit of a tomboy – and of course she now works as a personal trainer in a fancy health centre, doesn't she? She's always been a bit on the sporty side, if you know what I mean. Not that it always means you'll turn out like my Alison. But it's often an indication, isn't it? I mean, you're quite sporty-looking, aren't you, if you don't mind me saying. But then again, there's other sporty women who aren't like my Alison at all, like that Sue Barker – I don't think she is, 'cos she likes Cliff Richard, doesn't she? And my Alison doesn't at all. And then again there's girls like my Alison who don't look particularly sporty at all, like you! *(She points at someone in the audience.)*

So, anyway, it was a couple of Christmases ago now that Alison first told me. She calls up, and I've got my hand halfway up a turkey, and she says, "Mum, is it OK for me to bring my lover down for Christmas?" So I goes, "Well, who do you mean exactly?" And she gets all in lather and goes, "Well, if you're going to be like that then we'll go somewhere else where we're both wanted!"

So I says, "Hold your horses." I says, "I only said that because, as you well know, where we live, 'my lover', that could mean anyone from your girlfriend to the man in the fish and chip shop. Now, this lover of yours, is she a vegetarian? 'Cos if she doesn't eat turkey and I have to cook another vegetable, well, I won't be able to manage it, not with only three rings working properly."

And after that it was just fine. Helen, she was a lovely girl. Very polite about my stuffing, as I recall. But anyway, we all got on like a house on fire and come Easter time I said to Alison, "If you'd like to invite Helen down for the bank holiday, I'd love to see her again." But Alison goes, "Erm, well, Mum, the thing is… I've finished with Helen, I'm with Suki now."

"Oh," I says. "Right," I says. "Well, you can bring her down if you like," I says. So, that's how I met Suki and she was a nice girl too – not as nice as Helen mind – but then my Alison finished with Suki and there was one I didn't meet, Wendy. And then there was Andrea – now, she was nice, but she had to go back to New Zealand – and then there was Penny. That's the one she's with now. Not so keen on her myself. But I don't say nothing, me. Try not to interfere. Alison's got to make her own choices in life. Isn't that right? It's not up to me to choose who she goes out with. Mind you, you look like a nice girl *(pointing out a woman in the audience)*. Are you single? Do you live near here? On a good salary? I could give you her number if you like.

Sorry. None of my business.

I just want her to be happy. That's all. And I want to understand a bit more about her world. So I don't say the wrong thing or nothing. I just want to be supportive, you know? Like last summer when I come up to do the Pride march with her. Now some of the frocks them boys were wearing! They were beautiful! Alison couldn't have made anything like that. She didn't keep up with her domestic science at school. Swapped over to woodwork as soon as she could, didn't she? No, she was just wearing shorts and a T-shirt on the march and walking boots. All the girls were. You need sensible shoes for a long march, don't you? Can't be teetering around in high heels, like the boys do, that's just silly.

And then we was singing all the way along. And we had a laugh, and a drink, and we met some lovely folk. Then we went back on the tube. Got some funny looks, mind, on the way home, when I started singing some of the songs I'd learnt on the march: "She'll be coming with a woman when she comes..." Do you know that one? "She'll be coming with a woman when she comes." Bit rude, isn't it? Sing along if you do. "She'll be coming with a woman, coming with a woman, coming with a woman when she comes!"

Lovely meeting you all, bye for now! Bye!

# I'M A "WE"

I'll never forget that first night when we met 'cos they say
That opposites often attract and it happened that way.
You laughed at my views and I thought you were talking such rot.
I felt glum, you seemed fun,
You were short, I was blonde, you were not.

I lived south of the river, the worst part of London, you claim,
But as lesbians do, you moved in the next day all the same.
The flat looked a mess with your things in and I like it neat
And I wondered how cooking would work since you didn't eat
    meat.

    But now people claim
    We're exactly the same.
    They say time has shown
    I'm becoming a clone.
    Where once we fell out,
    We now tend to agree,
    But I'm happy to shout:
    I'm no longer an "I", I'm a "We".

We've got the same haircuts and glasses and phones that we chose
And when you lost weight it made sense that we shared the same
    clothes.
My mother calls up and you answer the phone and she starts:
"Now which one of you is that? I can't tell your voices apart."

We used to be different – so much so, it caused quite a fuss.
Now we see that the world's got it wrong and it's "Them versus
Us".
We thank heaven above that we've both learned to love the same
things:
It works out much cheaper and makes our love deeper –
In fact, we've exchanged the same rings.

And now people claim
We're exactly the same.
They say we're on the brink
Of talking in sync.
And if you should doubt
I've lost all sense of me,
Well you're right
'Cos I'm happy to shout:
I'm no longer an "I", I'm a "We"!

# HAPPY TOGETHER

My girlfriend and I are very happy together. It's not always easy to make a lesbian relationship really work but I think we manage quite well. All things considered. Yes, we've had our problems... in fact, looking back, I can see that they probably started just after the initial honeymoon period. That was such a wonderful time! All that sex. Talking into the night about our past lovers. Doing it in the shower for the first time. Roses, romance and a heart-fluttering hope that this really could be the woman of my dreams.

And then it all goes wrong. Well... not exactly "wrong", but it becomes somehow different. The sex goes for a start. OK, so it doesn't exactly "go", it just changes. First it's there, then it's gone. I suppose that's quite a change, isn't it? But then you can settle down to something a little more comfortable and secure... albeit perhaps a little more boring. And that's when you start to window shop. Well not me, but my partner, she did. She said she just wanted to make sure that she was with the right person. She'd look at some gorgeous dyke across a crowded bar and think, "All right, she may be good looking, but I bet she couldn't cook Spaghetti Carbonara just the way I like it... the way Clare makes it for me... Or could she?" So she'd buy the woman a drink anyway and then find out that she spoke no English and was going back to Latvia the following day and she'd come back home to me, her chosen partner.

But as the months went by I could tell she was restless. One day I had it out with her and she said that she felt she was missing something in her life. I suggested that perhaps she might be missing me since she hadn't been home for the last three weeks. She told me about this other woman she'd been seeing called Sarah. I didn't really want to know the details. Well, apart from how often, when,

26

where, why, what positions, who came and how many times? She told me that it had all been a terrible mistake. She said I must understand that she was still young, impressionable, easily led... I suggested that perhaps "unfaithful" might be the word that she was ineffectively groping for.

She said she'd made a choice. She wanted to come back to me if I'd have her.

Suddenly in a burst of sisterly compassion I asked whether this "Sarah" woman might be broken-hearted to lose her, but she informed me that Sarah's girlfriend had now come back from America where she'd been working for a couple of months teaching karate... and was there any chance I'd agree to making our phone number ex-directory?

My girlfriend said that she'd seen the error of her ways. She told me that she'd always regard me as her "Core" relationship. I said, "'Cor' as in 'Cor blimey, how gullible can one woman be?'" But she said, "No, as in a very special relationship. A true meeting of minds and souls."

I remember at the time thinking, "Isn't that what people say when they want to keep you as a friend but get off with someone else as well?" But I let it go because she said she really did still want me as a lover.

And after all that we're still together. We're a "Couple". We live together. Get asked to parties together. Take the cats to the vet together. All right, we don't actually sleep together, but that's because she says I snore sometimes, and my bed's no good for her back, and she gets up earlier than me. But apart from that, we're very happy together.

It's not always easy to make a lesbian relationship really work, but I think we manage quite well... all things considered.

# TEXAS

*Lights come on to reveal Clare in handcuffs and a blindfold with her legs bound together.*

God, this feels weird! Not bad weird, just weird weird, if you know what I mean! Have you ever done this with anyone else? I bet you have. Are you sure I shouldn't have taken my clothes off *before* you tied me up? I just thought that might have been a bit sexier?

So, where did you get all this stuff from then? I am assuming that they're new and not borrowed, or from some previous relationship? In which case that must mean that you've recently been to a sex shop without me. Am I right? I do hope you didn't get anything in rubber. Susan? Tell me you're not dressing up in rubber, 'cos I'm sorry but I think it looks disgusting.

*(Pause.)*

Oh I see, I'm going to get the silent treatment, am I? OK, so what happens now? Am I meant to tell you that I've been a naughty girl, or something?

Actually, darling, before we go on, I think we should both agree on a "safe" word, don't you? You know, like it said in that article? It said it was really important to sort that out before you start. But remember, you can't have something like "Stop" 'cos that could actually mean, "I think I could manage a little more," and you shouldn't have a name that you call each other usually, like "Bunnykins" or something, 'cos you might say that anyway, and not mean for the other person to stop what they're doing. So I think we should decide on something before we go on, don't you?

Let's have a think...

*(Brief pause.)*

OK. OK. I've thought of one. How about "Sharleen Spiteri"? You know, the singer out of Texas? She's nice. Actually, I'm not sure if we're allowed to choose a name and not a word, because, well, someone might think that the other person wanted them to be that person. Do you know what I mean?

So how about I just say "Texas"? Hey, did you know that Texas is an anagram of At Sex... so that's quite good, isn't it? And it's a bit shorter anyway, because I might need a word I can say really quickly, should the need arise!

You know, they always say that trust is a really important part of S&M, don't they? And I can see that now, 'cos it's like you have to put all your trust completely into the other person when you're doing this kind of thing, don't you?

Susan? Don't you agree? Look, I'm going to take this blindfold off now 'cos it's getting really itchy. OK?

*(She does so with a certain amount of difficulty. Then she looks – or rather jumps – around the room looking for Susan. The realisation dawns that she is on her own.)*

*(Under her breath.)* When you come home you are so dead...

*(She sees a note on the table and reads it aloud.)*

Dear Clare,
You said last night that you thought our sex life was getting a little dull, so I thought I'd try something a bit different.
She's called "Andrea". I met her last week at the gym.
She's very cute and doesn't say an awful lot – which, to be perfectly honest, is a bit of a welcome break.
Susan
PS: I'll call next week to discuss custody of the laptop, when you're a little less tied up.

Oh, ha bloody ha!

# MAGGIE MAYBE

I have fancied older women all my life. In kindergarten I used to wish I could stay behind after school with Miss Cooley, whom I assumed lived in the classroom. When I was ten, I remember crying when my games teacher told me that she was going to leave at the end of the term to get married; and when I was fifteen, Miss Boxall became my history teacher. Miss Boxall was – and still remains – the greatest love of my life.

After I left school, I continued to be attracted by older and wiser women on whom I could develop a crush – and if they looked anything like Miss Boxall, well, that was an added bonus. Tutors at college, directors in acting jobs and inevitably, in later years, any therapist who would take my money.

But the one thing that all the women I love have in common is that every single one of them has shown absolutely no interest in me. As an adult, I can now see that this makes perfect sense, since I know that unattainable love is and always has been a lesbian's trademark. And at school you couldn't get more unattainable than Miss Boxall. She was a teacher, she was straight and she was completely unaware of my existence. The perfect lesbian crush. I probably still love Miss Boxall more than I've ever loved any other woman since.

Which is partly the reason I had arranged to meet my best friend, Annie, at a somewhat chic and overpriced gay restaurant in West London on a rainy night in February. Not, I hasten to add, to discuss my embarrassing behaviour in the presence of my history teacher two decades ago, but to update her on the latest news about my ever-disastrous love life. I'd finally split up with Steph: "Late forties, professional woman, good sense of humour, wants to share fun times out and quiet nights in…" but obviously hadn't wanted to share the fact that she already had a girlfriend whom, I'd since found out, she carried on seeing all through our relationship.

So I had to update Annie with all the latest events of the little lesbian drama that I call my life. The screaming rows, incriminating accusations, hysterical sobbing, followed by a leaden heartache and a very slight flutter of relief when Steph gave me back the keys to my flat, which hopefully meant that deep down I'd done the right thing by finally telling her to get lost.

Once I'd finished my initial rant and got Annie up to speed, I paused to throw some much-needed wine down my throat, which gave Annie the chance she'd been waiting for to start her "I told you so's". They were as predictable as usual and annoyingly accurate, but since I couldn't remember one time when she had ever approved of anyone I'd ever been out with (since her), I took them with a pinch of salt.

Over the years it wasn't just Annie who had continually worried about my choice of girlfriends. To be perfectly honest, I too was beginning to doubt my own judgement in that area. Once again I found myself coming back to that inescapable question: "Why can't I find someone normal?"

As I polished off the garlic bread and Annie polished off her third cigarette, I looked around the restaurant to see where the waiter might have got to with our main course. I noticed that most of the customers were gay men with cheeky smiles and perfect pecs. There were two women on the table next to ours who looked decidedly straight but hey, what do I know about these things? And a couple of dykes over at a window table. One of them caught my eye because, even though her back was turned to me, I thought that she looked a little bit like my old history teacher. Well, about twenty years older than she was then, of course. Now *there* was a woman I would have stayed with forever.

Suddenly she turned round and I saw her face. My heart quite literally stopped. Oh my God. It was her. It was Maggie Boxall! There was no mistaking it. There she was, my old, supposedly straight, married, mother of two, history teacher, in the flesh and only a few yards away from me. There was nothing for it, I did what any other self-respecting, besotted, love-stricken lesbian would have done under the circumstances. I dived head-first under my table and hid from her sight under the safety of a large white tablecloth.

My mind raced back through time to my adolescent years when I had last seen her. Those days when everything I did or said around her involved some odd, embarrassing behaviour on my part and resulted in weary, bemused looks from Miss Boxall. Or "Maggie" as I was later to call her.

I had known that Miss Boxall's first name began with an "M" but it wasn't until I got her to sign my rough book so that I could get a new one from the stationery office that I found out that the "M" stood for Maggie. I copied her signature out several times just for the thrill of it and then I went down to the shops and bought the record "Maggie May" by Rod Stewart. After three days of locking myself in my room, playing truant from school and listening to that particular song several hundred times through, I became convinced that it was in fact Maggie Boxall who had "led me away from school, because she didn't want to be a fool – she stole my heart and that's a pain I could do without".

Miss Boxall never actually told me which road she lived in, but she obviously wanted me to visit because during one of her lessons she mentioned that she had a stream running at the bottom of her garden. Well, I knew that she lived in a certain village in Kent, which for legal reaons and for the purposes of protecting her anonymity shall remain nameless. (Kemsing.)

So that night, Ordnance Survey map in hand, I cycled there and traced the routes of any rivers and streams within a six-mile radius of the village, until I finally came across a likely road and my heart skipped a beat as I saw her car parked in one of the driveways. I have a very vague memory of it now.

I think it might have been a blue Mini, registration number XPR 482G. I was the original lesbian stalker.

After that discovery, there was no turning back. I had found a shrine at which to worship and, night after night, I would cycle there and position myself across the other side of the road from her house. Looking at her car, her driveway, her windows. Looking for what? Well, I suppose just a passing glimpse of her would have been thrilling to the extreme, but there seemed little chance of that ever happening. It was, after all, evening time and dark and winter and the curtains were always drawn. But every once in a while someone would brush against them and they would move ever so slightly and my heart would leap into my mouth.

Perhaps she might look out now. Perhaps she might see me in the shadows. Perhaps she might enact a little script that I had going around in my head that went something like this:

MAGGIE: *(Drawing curtain)* Is that Clare Summerskill from Lower Five B? What on earth could she be doing outdoors on a night as cold as this? I must go and talk to her... Hello, you poor little thing, what in heaven's name are you doing out here in the rain?

CLARE: *(Shivering slightly)* Hello, Miss Boxall. I hope I haven't disturbed you from your book marking?

MAGGIE: Not at all! I'm just glad that I saw you. Now I insist that you come into my house immediately and I'll make you some hot soup and dry your hair with a towel by the fire. It's quite apparent to me that you must come from a totally dysfunctional family who neglect you terribly. I see that I shall have to apply for adoption papers first thing in the morning and then tell my husband to move out while you come and live with me instead.

Well, that's how the script ran. But, spoilsport that she was, Maggie Boxall never played along. And, as you might already have guessed, she never adopted me either. She never so much as opened the curtains.

And now, hidden under a restaurant table, I was trying desperately to gather my thoughts in a calm and collected manner. I think I might have been vaguely aware of Annie's concerned voice asking me if I was all right but all I could think about was what I'd say to Maggie Boxall once I had summoned the courage to get up. For twenty years I'd dreamed of this very moment when I would meet Maggie as an adult. And in my head I had a little script that she might enact that went something like this:

MAGGIE: Is that really Clare Summerskill from Lower Five B, over there in this gay restaurant? I must go over and speak to her. Hello. Fancy seeing you in a place like this!

ME: *(Trembling with excitement)* Is it really you, Maggie, after all this time?

MAGGIE: Yes, and you were right all along, I am a lesbian but it just took me a while to find out. But I'm single at the moment. I don't suppose luck would have it that you are too?

Well, that's how the script ran and now was the time to try it out for real. I decided to bite the bullet, face the music, screw my courage to the sticking point and use as many metaphors as I could in one sentence. I stood up abruptly, momentarily forgetting about my foetal position and banging my head quite violently on the underside of the table, screaming loudly as I did so. The crockery and the glasses on the table clattered their way to the floor and spilt their contents over me as they went flying.

But still my resolve to speak to Maggie held firm and, visibly shaking, with my shirt and trousers now drenched in wine, I stood up and started walking over to the window. As I did, I noticed that the table where she had been sitting was being cleared. Both the women had disappeared. I glanced over at the counter to see if they were settling their bill and then I ran to the door and looked up and down the street.

I rushed back to my table and asked Annie: "Did you see her go?"

"See who go?" Annie asked.

"The woman at the table by the window."

"Erm... yes, I think some women did leave around the same time as you got up and knocked the table over. I expect they probably went to find somewhere a bit quieter to eat."

To this day I'll never know if Maggie left because she saw that it was me making a spectacle of myself yet again, or if that was just a coincidence. Annie says that it probably never was Maggie in the first place, just wishful thinking on my part. Annie thinks that I should learn to live in a more reality-based world and that I should start looking for a girlfriend who isn't a) totally unattainable or b) non-existent, but more importantly c) is my own age and d) is one that she can get on with. So I told Annie that, as usual, she was right and that I would try my hardest to find someone fitting that description.

But I hate to make promises I know I can never keep.

# THE THERAPY YEARS

Right then. OK. So what happens now? I haven't actually done this before. Therapy, I mean.

*(Pause.)*

Why did I come to see you? Well, erm, let's see. Some people may have suggested that it might, you know, help me a bit. My girlfriend, in particular – sorry, my *EX*-girlfriend, she used to say that I needed therapy. Well, she didn't actually *say* it so much as sort of shout it, you know, loudly in public places. Usually when we were having a row and she wasn't getting her own way. She used to say that I had a big problem about my jealousy, but my argument would be that anyone would get in a state if they had a girlfriend who shagged anything that moved and then lied pathologically about it and made it seem like I was the one with the problem.

What? Do I trust her judgement? You wouldn't ask me that if you'd seen her *new* girlfriend! *(Laughs.)*

Yes I *am* aware that humour is a powerful form of defence.

*(Slight pause.)*

And before you say it, I know that I am probably a little bit upset about splitting up with my girlfriend, but I'm sure that after a certain period of time combined with a few slightly cruel but somewhat humorous acts of revenge, I'll be able to get over her and move on with my life...

*(Tears well up, then Clare begins to howl.)*

She said she loved me. She said she'd never leave me. I don't care how many women she's slept with, I just want her back!

*(She snuffles a bit longer and finally calms down.)*

Can I just ask, why is the clock facing you and not me? I mean, I need to know how long I've got as well, don't I?

No, I'm not changing the subject.

What? Am I still in love with her? Of course not! God! I mean, as if! After what she's done. I am *so* over that woman, I can't tell you. I mean, I can barely even remember her name now, that is just *how* insignificant she was to me. All right, I do remember her name, it's Maria. You don't know her, do you?

*(Pause.)*

You don't say an awful lot, do you? You know, for the £45. I expect that's deliberate though, isn't it? To give me time to talk without being interrupted and to work things out for myself. And I do have certain things to sort out now, I know that.

Like, what to do with her birthday present. I got us tickets to see Mary Chapin Carpenter in concert. 'Cos that's how we met. Well, we were both at this party and I was dancing to one of Mary's tracks, and I was a bit drunk and anyway I spilt my drink over this woman next to me, and when I looked up, our eyes sort of locked together and I knew from that moment that this was going to be a big one for me. So then we both went to get a cloth and in the corridor she gave me this really passionate kiss and then... Sorry?

We've run out of time? Oh, right.

Well, I don't know. Do *you* think I need to come back? Yes, yes, of course I do. Silly question. Right then. Now, next week I'm free Monday, Tuesday, Wednesday... or Thursday...

Friday three o'clock? Fine.

And your rates are going up from? ... Next week, right.

OK then, thanks a lot. Thank you. Bye. See you then. Cheers. Bye.

## REVENGE SONG

We've been together forever it seems
And we always agreed if it ended, we'd be
Full of love and respect for the changes ahead,
So I can't understand why I just want you dead.

Perhaps it is something to do with the fact
That you've told me you're leaving and not coming back.
You've been seeing someone else without me ever knowing
And I want to stay calm but my anger is showing.

    Here's some of the things that I'm wishing for you:
    That all of your whites will become tinted blue,
    That whatever your lottery numbers, you lose,
    And there's always a hold-up at the checkout you choose.

My therapist tells me I have to move on –
I must grieve you and leave you to go where you've gone.
But I feel deep inside that you won't get too far
'Cos I've hidden both sets of the keys to your car.

I hope that the cat pees on your favourite chair
And that grey will start showing quite soon in your hair,
And I know you love tennis, so next on my list
Is you slip on the pavement and fracture your wrist.

    Here's what I'm wishing by way of goodbye:
    I want all of the plants in your garden to die;
    And I hope your new girlfriend will dump you real soon
    And when you call me in tears I'll be over the moon.

I hope when you play golf your handicap rises
And you start over-eating and go up three sizes.
I hope you find damp in the flat that you're buying
And that airport delays happen each time you're flying.

I hope that our friends take my side and agree
That your new shag could never be nicer than me,
And I wish all your email addresses deleted,
Then my sweet revenge will be partially completed.

I'd like to be kind and I'd like to stand tall
And to tell you I'm not feeling bitter at all,
But I can't do the right thing and wish you good luck
'Cos you're with someone else, so I don't give a f**k!

# FENNEL

Well, hello everyone, my name's Fennel – and can I just say, I'm experiencing an amazing chi energy from everyone else here, right now in this room! Except for, wait a minute, someone over in this area, where I can feel that the energy's a little blocked and congested. Would that be right? Actually, you don't have to answer that, I just want you to think maybe about redistributing your meridians, OK? Anyway, the thing is that I hardly ever find myself in a large group these days, since we moved away from London, me and my girlfriend.

We used to live in Hampstead in a very big house there with loads of rooms and everything and we were both doing what they call "proper" jobs and one day we just thought: "We may be very very rich in monetary terms, so why is it that we just feel so spiritually impoverished?" So me and Camomile – well that wasn't her name when she was working in the City, but she changed it – anyway, we wanted to just, like, get out of the rat race and we decided to downsize and we bought this beautiful farm in the countryside and we lived there for quite a while on the money that we'd made from the sale.

And this farm we bought was just like so fantastic and it had all these animals all over the place which was just amazing and the people we bought it from said that we had to look after them, which we did, but then we found out that every year we were meant to send most of them off somewhere to be killed. Apparently that's how farmers make their living. But how can anyone be expected to do that? I mean, animals are human beings too. And when you've made friends with them and given them all names and let them sleep at the bottom of the bed, which is what we used to do with the goats... Well, we just couldn't buy into that cruelty, so we decided

to sell the farm and downsize again – this time to a beautiful little cottage with a really good energy to it – and we lived on the profit of the sale for a while. And we had a vegetable garden and we were trying to live as self-sufficiently as we possibly could, but of course there are some things that you can't grow like chocolate and Rioja and, well, quite a lot of stuff really, but there was a Sainsbury's megastore quite nearby so it never got critical.

But then the money we'd made from selling the farm eventually ran out, so we had to downsize again, but it really didn't matter because at the end of the day we had each other and that was all we needed.

And once you've experienced living in a totally spiritual and unmaterialistic way, there's really no going back to your old life, because on this planet we have nothing more than our bodies, which are the sacred vessels that carry us through life, and our wombs, which are the boats through which we travel to other dimensions. And Camomile and I – we live with such a deep love and respect for each other and a total contentment with all that we have, which is actually in fact now a small caravan. Because after a while in the cottage, the money we'd saved started running a little low, so we decided to downsize again. But it's a really beautiful caravan with a beautiful energy to it.

And I'm trying to earn a little money now as a sculptress. I make figurines of mermaids from old fizzy drink cans, which as you've probably already worked out actually represents the transformation of commercial materialism into an artistic depiction of the mother goddess. And I sell them on a stall by the roadside. Well, I haven't actually sold any yet but that's because people drive by too fast to notice that I'm there, which, if you think about it, is quite symbolic of everything I've been talking about. How much you can miss out on in life if you're always going too fast.

And Camomile has started to do drum making, which is a really beautiful thing, and sometimes in the evening under the moon, she'll be playing the drums and I'll join in with her on the penny whistle and then she'll ask me not to, because she says I'm not very good yet and it sounds horrible. So then I'll just dance to the sound of her drums, knowing that the choreography of the dances of the universe is endless and my dance is an expression of my own beauty and is always unique to me.

But actually Camomile has mentioned that we're getting a little low on finances again so we might have to sell the caravan soon. But we've recently bought a lovely little tepee that we can move into which is really beautiful and has a lovely energy and the man who owns the field we're in says that we can stay there right up to the point when the developers start work. So you see, we are truly blessed and we've got each other and what more would we ever need... apart from maybe a Portaloo – that would be quite handy, actually.

Right, I'm going to leave you with a beautiful saying that's always helped me a lot and I hope it means something to you too: "When I am stuck in mud, I go to the water and she moves me with her passion."

Thank you.

# SINGLE AGAIN

I wouldn't say categorically that Susan was into S&M but it is true that she tied me to the bed post one night... and then left me there while she went off to see her new girlfriend. Our relationship ended quite amicably, all things considered. She got custody of the laptop, I got the printer. Once again it was time to search for a significant other. That's when I met Phil. Phil was stunning: the first dyke I'd ever been out with who could make other women actually stop and stare. Phil was kind, generous, sweet, funny and sexy – and she was also pathologically unfaithful. After the fourth affair that she'd had while she'd been with me – or at least the fourth that I knew about – I finally told her in no uncertain terms that since she had now gone so far to as to move in with her latest floozy, I had no alternative but to finish our relationship.

After that fateful conversation, which I had hoped would bring her running back to me, I hadn't seen Phil again. The following weeks were absolute hell. Long drawn out days of depression and loneliness with only the familiar casts of *Neighbours*, *Home and Away*, *Emmerdale*, *Coronation Street* and *Eastenders* to keep me company.

On bad days, I drank myself into a stupor, waking up sometime the following afternoon and glancing pathetically over at the answerphone to see if she might have left me a loving message while I'd been unconscious. I began to hate the very sight of that bloomin' nought.

Phil had finally left me for a bisexual woman who worked in a beauty salon in the day and took an evening class in business studies. How politically low can you stoop? And after ten weeks she eventually called to tell me that Miss Best Of Both Worlds had decided she had been forcibly seduced and corrupted by Phil and had now gone back to men, who she claimed were "much simpler beings".

I didn't think that things could get much worse than they already were, but then Phil informed me that even though she was now single and homeless, she still didn't want to come and live with me. I tried to look on the bright side. Maybe things weren't as bad as they seemed, if only I could just try and think a little more positively. I tried to remember something my therapist had once said about a glass of water and different ways of looking at it but instead my mind started working out how much someone could earn in a week if they charged £45 an hour.

I forced my attention back to the matter in hand. Right, so there I was, a lesbian alone in London. Now, how should I go about meeting other women? "I don't have to get off with someone, I just want to widen my circle of friends," I tried to convince myself, my cat and a rather nice woman with a Scottish accent that I sometimes got through to at the Lesbian and Gay Switchboard.

For one scary moment I even considered putting a personal ad in *Diva*, but the thought that someone might recognise it as me made me change my mind. So instead I decided to dip my metaphorical toe in the pool of social frenzy that is The Brixton Hill Lesbian Social Group Gathering.

One Tuesday evening, I spent three-quarters of an hour sitting round a pub table with four other sad and desperate dykes. A woman called Charlotte ran these evenings, though I'm not sure why, since she was clearly not by nature a very sociable type. She grunted a hello at me when I arrived and said nothing more. Two of the others were a couple, Sandra and Sue. Sandra was a little on the butch side and she told me straight away that they were both interested in meeting new women with the intention of a threesome. They asked me things like "Have you been to the Candy Bar yet?" and "Do you like k.d. lang? We do!"

The other woman there was German. She was called Ingrid and wore a pair of rather scary rectangular glasses. She talked to me about the strength of the Euro against the pound and told me that she spoke four other languages. I assumed that her conversation would be equally as dull in all of them.

After what I considered to be a polite amount of time, I suddenly exclaimed that I'd left some stock boiling and had to tend to it immediately. Outside on the pavement an important truth hit me harder than the cold night air: that it isn't always better to have tried and failed than never to have tried at all.

I had nearly run out of ideas when I happened upon an "alternative" way of meeting women. It came in the form of a leaflet that I'd picked up while visiting my homeopath. It was for a wild women's weekend in Wales. I read through it carefully:

"Are you at peace with yourself internally?

Do you feel in touch with the source of your creativity?

Do you yearn for a closer connection to the elements?"

The answer to these questions I could not in all honesty tell you, but there was one more which was in my head but not to be found on the leaflet:

"Do you feel precariously close to running out of ideas of how to ever meet anyone ever again?"

The answer came as a resounding "Yes!"


And so it was that I set off for a sacred site in the north of Wales to discover the mysteries of psychic and spiritual healing. To listen to the silence, to fly with the eagle, to learn about the wonders of starcraft, herbal lore and plant spirits and to try with all my shamanic body and soul to get just one single shag out of the next few days.

Predictably enough there was a torrential downpour as soon as I arrived. The organisers had thought it would create a magical feeling for the tents to nestle on the slopes of the mountain, but the rain produced a landslide of mud and stones and we all just stood and watched helplessly as the entire campsite slid down the hill towards a lake. We ran for safety towards the main house with plastic bags over our heads and spent the afternoon drying our clothes on radiators. On the Sunday, the tents were for some inexplicable reason repitched, even though there might well be more rain to come. I felt compelled to join in one of the activities, so I plumped for drum-making. But by camomile tea-time I had decided that I was the only person there who might possibly escape being sectioned if anyone from social services had dropped by.

One more night to go and I would be free from this seriously disturbed group of women, most of whom were straight and thought that it was really exciting to be free from their men for two days in the year. Asleep in my little tent, dreaming of meat and mattresses, I was suddenly awoken by a woman who introduced herself as Tanya and who, without asking, came in to join me.

My first impression was that she might have overdosed on the contents of her medicine wheel because her eyes were very slightly crazed, but perhaps more significant was the fact that she was completely naked. She leant right over me as she spoke, waving her huge pendulous bosoms in my face, and it would have taken a far stronger woman than I not to have been somewhat distracted as she began to tell me that astrologically it was a very important date and would I come out and share the wonders and delights of the Big Dipper with her?

I told Tanya, as politely as I could, "Thank you, but no." I really had to get some sleep. But she burst into tears and between sobs informed me that since she'd been adopted as a child she had always taken rejection very badly and had an enormous need to be loved. She then took my hand in hers and placed it between her thighs, telling me that she had always wanted a lesbian experience and would I satisfy her curiosity?

I was far too tired to deal with any conflict resolution at that point, even though, coincidentally, there had been a workshop on that very subject earlier in the weekend. The sooner I got on with it, the sooner I might get some kip.

I performed the necessary act upon her, not completely unaware that the entire reputation of my lesbian sisters was at stake. But the loud wailing noises that she emitted convinced me that I hadn't let the side down. She then proceeded to snore rather loudly and took up so much of the lilo that she forced me to spend the rest of the night on the groundsheet.

The next day I felt mortified. I had never had a one-night stand in my entire life and, looking at Tanya over a bowl of muesli, I realised that (whether it was politically correct or not) in the clear light of day there was no way I would ever have touched this particular woman with a bargepole.

She said that she'd send me a postcard from Canada where she was going next on a bear and whale watching trip and I wished her all the best with her travels. As we parted I prayed that I would never hear from her again.

I returned to my London flat exhausted. I checked the answerphone and saw that there was one message. My heart leapt into my mouth – I hadn't had a message in weeks.

Maybe Phil had changed her mind. Maybe she'd missed me while I'd been gone and my unannounced absence had driven her into a fit of possessive jealousy. Maybe I might consider taking her back and then one evening casually mention that she wasn't the only one who'd been sowing their oats, that my life too had recently been altered by a brief but meaningful liaison with a wild, wild woman up a mountain. I held my breath and pressed "Play".

"Hello, this is Sandra, of Sandra and Sue."

My heart sank. But then I told myself that if this was the only offer I was ever going to receive from a real lesbian – or in this case, lesbians – then perhaps I should stop being so fussy and accept it. The message continued: "We were just wondering if you had Ingrid's number, as we thought we'd like to see a bit more of her, if you know what I mean! Call me when you get this message. Bye."

# MARY

*Mary is middle-aged, bespectacled and quietly spoken.*

Hello. My name's Mary. I live with my partner Monica, in a little cottage. We moved out to the country a few years ago. I was a primary school teacher and Monica worked in accounts at the DHSS so we both led quite a hectic city life! But nowadays, do you know what my main concern is in life? Getting rid of the molehills in the garden. I'm not joking. They're destroying it. I'm going to have to get the mole-catcher in. I've no choice. I can't go through another restless night worrying that, as I'm laying there quietly in my bed, a little mole is trying its level best to destroy the dream garden we've fought our whole lives to acquire.

Now you might have noticed that I said *my* bed and that's because we're sleeping apart at the moment, Monica and me. Nothing serious, mind. Just that one of us has got a little snoring problem. I won't say who... But you see, Monica is a bit of a carpentry wizard... Oh yes, and she's been working with a lot of sawdust recently 'cos she's also a builder. Not by trade, of course, but she's always been good at DIY and that sort of thing. Like a lot of lesbians seem to be. Funny, isn't it? Not me, I'm more of a garden sort of person. I like potting and digging. So we're always busy. When we bought the place, it was almost derelict, but Monica's ever so clever, she's rebuilt the whole cottage around the original fireplace. I could show you the photo book if you like. Before and after. It's absolutely fascinating! Anyway, she reroofed the place and she's currently working on a small extension. But there's still so much to do and she's often up at dawn to get started and then I won't really see her to talk to till I call her in for the evening meal. So even though we live together, I don't feel we see as much of each other as I'd like.

Which is probably why, sometimes, I feel a little isolated here. I mean, they're friendly enough in the village. And people always say hello to Goldie – she's our Labrador. But there's been no dinner or party invites. Nothing like that. So, one day I thought to myself: "Well, there's got to be other lesbians like us living in little cottages around this part of the country. I wonder if there's some sort of a way that we can all find out about each other?"

So, I wrote some little cards and put them all around the libraries and the farm shops and so on, in the area, seeking out other like-minded women. Well, only a few months later I got a reply from another couple who live in a village about twenty miles away! So we all got in contact... Well, I say "we", but it was just me and them actually, because Monica had an important delivery of concrete arriving that morning, so I drove over with Goldie and I met them. Lovely women they were, living in a little cottage, just like us, but without the building work going on. Pat and Pamela, they're called. And it was from meeting them that I decided to start a newsletter for lesbians in the countryside.

And that's how "Walkin' (with an apostrophe) Women" came into being. And it's been going now for nearly two years. And I'm the editor. And the features writer. And the photographer. And the circulation has gone up again this summer – it's now seven, which I'm quietly pleased about – and it's full of information that other women like us would find helpful. There's the lesbian cinema-visiting group. That's called "Flicks for Chicks" (I thought that up myself). And then we have visits of general interest. That section's called "Interesting Women". With the two meanings of the word, you see. And it's all properly arranged. Last month we went on a tour of our local town's postal sorting office. Now, not many turned out for that one. Just me and Pamela, but it *was* quite interesting, as it happens. And next month we've got a lesbian speaker (that'll be Pat) doing a talk about mushrooms, with a guided woodland walk included and a pub lunch as well. So that should be fun.

Any road, I'd love to sit around and chat all day but I do have to get on because I've got an internet class to go to. Oh yes, I'm not one to let the grass grow under my feet, in any sense of the word. I'm going to learn how to put the group up on the worldwide web.

Imagine that! www.walkin-(with an apostrophe)-women dot com, or dot co uk, I'm not sure. But hey, listen to me and my IT talk! And to think it wasn't so very long ago when I thought that software was a nice comfortable fleece. Heigh-ho! Must go! Cheerio!

# LUCY: CHECK IT OUT

*Lucy is a young "happening" cyber dyke.*

Is it just me or are these lights really bright in here? I'm still feeling a bit rough from last night. And the night before. I really need to sort myself out, man, and get in shape. I have joined my local gym up the road. It's wicked there. You can watch MTV when you're on the jogging machines. Well I haven't actually tried it out yet, but it looked really good when they showed me around. And I know I *should* go... but like, this morning, for example, I was definitely going to go but I was asleep, and then this afternoon I was going to but something happened... Oh yes, I got really depressed. And before you ask, no it wasn't what I took last night. 'Cos that's really good gear. It's not that, it's that's cow Joanne, isn't it? Yeah 'cos she was there at the Sweetie Wrapper Bar last night. Typical! All over Ellie, it was gross, man!

Sometimes I think it's shit being a lesbian 'cos if you were straight you wouldn't have to sit there and watch two of your exes getting it together right in front of your face every time you go out. I have to call ahead when I go for a drink – call my friend, DJ Nina, who works there – and I go, "All right, DJ Nina," and she goes, "All right, Lucy," and she tells me if they've been in. But last night they got there just after I'd arrived. God, it was so awful. I just wanted to beat the crap out of her. But I just got really pissed instead which is the more mature thing to do, isn't it? And at closing time I was just about to go up to her and tell her what I really thought of her, but I had to go to the toilet and throw up and when I came back they'd gone.

But also it gives lesbians a bad name, doesn't it? When they do that sort of thing. Getting off with each other like that. 'Cos apart from no-marks like Joanne, it's quite cool to be gay now, isn't it?

Well, it is in London anyway. Well, in the Soho bit of London. And there's all these famous people coming out all the time, aren't there? Like Madonna kissing Britney Spears and that. Well, they don't actually say they're gay but the papers write that sort of stuff about them, which is really cool, isn't it? And soon everyone'll be fine about it, won't they?

I mean, I know in the old days it was more difficult and lesbians had to go round fighting for their rights, which was probably really tiring, but that's all done now and I think they should just chill out a bit and enjoy it. Like all the clubs and bars there are now. You've got so much choice. There's like the Sweetie Wrapper Bar or the Crystal Bar – well, that's only open at weekends – and the Last Inn, that's open in the daytime and it does really nice flapjacks there, and there's... Well, I can't think of anywhere else off the top of my head, but the point is, there's loads of gay places now, aren't there?

I'm thinking of setting up my own business. Maybe a gay bar or a nightclub. Cash in on the Pink Pound. I'm not sure yet. I'm still looking around. That's not my main line of work. No, I'm a graphic designer for my own lesbian website. It's called "I Love Lucy dot com". Check it out. But I'm also thinking of branching out into journalism 'cos I've got extensive experience in that as well. So it's just a question of which direction I take. But I've got time on my side. I'm only twenty-three next month. Twenty-three! Actually, that sounds quite old, doesn't it? Joanne's only twenty, but she's so pathetic, I don't know what I ever saw in her. God, I get so depressed just thinking about her. Look, can we talk about something else? Something that isn't to do with me and my exes!

Erm... erm... no, can't think of anything. Listen, I've got to take something for this headache before it turns into a migraine or a brain tumour. See ya around then. Check it out. Keep it real. Bye.

# DOING DIARIES

Terry? Darling? ... Well it's just that it's seven o'clock now. So... We did have something planned. Yes, we did arrange it... Yes, we did, darling. And it's on the kitchen calendar as well. Look. Seven o'clock, Saturday 4th, "Doing Diaries"? Hurrah! She finally remembers!

Right then. So if you get yours... OK. I thought perhaps we could go through things in order? ... Well, like your work, my work, Jennie and Luke, family, friends, and then all our social things after that.

OK. So you first.

Right *(writing it down as she says it)*. You've got late meetings next Tuesday, next Friday and the following Monday. OK. So I'll do the kids' teas then if you like. Fine. A conference in where? Hull? God! A week on Thursday overnight till Friday, back Friday evening late. OK. And a work do on the 17th. Am I invited to that? ... Oh. No, I just wanted to know. Yes, I'm sure I'd be bored silly.

No, *of course* I don't mind not coming.

OK! So! Is that it for you, work-wise, this month? At the moment. Right. Now, me.

Let's see... Erm... no. No, nothing as yet. Well, nothing finalised yet. And nothing to be finalised, in actual fact. But I've got that benefit coming up... that'll be sometime in November, but I thought it's probably better if we deal with that when we're "Doing Diaries" in October. What do you think? Great!

Now... Luke and Jennie. What have you got for them?

*(Writing)* Jennie's tap dance class on Monday. I could take her, if you like. I'm free. OK. Luke's dentist appointment on Tuesday... That's when you've got the meeting, isn't it? OK, I'll take him along. And Jennie's parents' evening on the 14th. I don't mind coming to that as well, if you want? For support...

No? OK then, it was just a thought. I was just trying to help.

No, darling, *of course* I don't mind not coming.

Right. Now do we know yet exactly what the kids are doing over the August bank holiday? Have you spoken to Bob? And is he having them? ... We've got them. OK.

Now, family and friends. What? ... No, look, I would definitely have remembered if you'd told me that your brother was coming to stay. Well, I suppose we can put him in my study... What? Well, I'll be in with you, of course.

Look, I don't see why I should have to sleep on the sofa when you'll have a double bed all to yourself! ... Well, maybe it's about time you did tell him! ... Yes, I know it's more complicated than that. I'm sorry. Look, darling, is it just the one night? ... Four weeks? And you'll both be away for the weekend of the 2nd, visiting your parents? Oh. I see. All right, I'll look after the kids, then.

No, darling, *of course* I don't mind not coming.

You know, Terry, your wretched brother aside, have you noticed that everything seems to be getting so busy and booked up these days? It's just that I'm feeling like we're hardly spending any real time together.

Yes, I know you've got a lot on at work, but, well, I can't remember the last time we got a chance to... you know, and I miss it, babes, I miss you. It's hard enough with Jennie and Luke around the whole time...

What? You've been wanting to do something about that too? Oh, aren't you a sweetie? So when exactly did *you* have in mind?

November 22nd?

What? No, darling, *of course* I don't mind not coming...

58

## WEDDING BELLS

I've got quite a difficult problem.
I need some advice, as it were.
My girlfriend's declared she's committed to me,
But I want to get shot of her.

We had fun at the start when I met her.
We got on then and life was a ball.
But now that she's said she's about to move in,
I know that she's not what I wanted at all

    And now that I feel we're inseparably bound,
    I'm not really sure that I like what I've found.
    And now I can hear wedding bells start to ring,
    I see that I really just wanted a fling.

The springtime of love was romantic.
We would dance every night until dawn
And laugh at those people who told us
That a Pisces shouldn't date a Capricorn.

And our love life was truly amazing –
The best sex that I'd ever known.
But now I just wait till she's snoring away,
'Cos I usually do it better on my own.

    And now that the flame of our love's burning low,
    I think that deep down I would like her to go.
    Just looking at rings makes me fill up with doubt.
    I feel claustrophobic and need to get out.

We went travelling the world with our rucksacks.
We were footloose and quite fancy-free.
But today she went shopping in Tesco's
And brought a turkey baster home for me.

I've tried to convert her to hip-hop
But she prefers Chris De Burgh's *Greatest Hits*,
And the age difference wasn't a problem at first
'Cos I loved all her tales of the Blitz.

But now that the magic has gone from our life,
The last thing I wanted from her was a wife.
And now that the field of our love's lying fallow,
I see that deep down she's really quite shallow.

So let's cut the crap 'cos I'm feeling quite stunned.
She's not what I wanted, I'd like a refund.
There's so many women I think I'd prefer –
I know what I want and it just isn't her!

# MARTINA

*Clare is wearing a cagoule and is sitting under an umbrella. She takes out a bit of paper and a pen from her bag and begins reading a letter she has just written.*

Dear Martina,

Firstly I would like to apologise for the appalling weather here in England. I know it hasn't stopped raining since you arrived. And now, as I put pen to paper, I am aware that you are at this very moment inside those famous changing rooms waiting for a chance to get out on court. If it's any comfort to you, Martina, I too have been waiting for quite a long time. I was in the queue this morning at seven to get a seat on Court One where you were scheduled to play. It is now eight o'clock in the evening and I have only seen seven games and they were between some rather elderly Australian men, which isn't the same thing at all. I am terrified of leaving my seat even for one minute just in case the rain stops for a bit and you appear for a knock-up. I now understand why players only take very small sips of their drinks between games.

I had the immense pleasure of seeing you play at Eastbourne two weeks ago. I was in the third row behind the umpire's chair, wearing a blue jacket. I don't expect you noticed me?

Anyway, I know one shouldn't really gloat but I was delighted when you put Betty Stove firmly in her place, 6-1, 6-love. She is rather a dour-looking woman, don't you agree, and appears to me to be a little too bulky for her chosen profession, particularly next to your lithe and muscular form.

I do not think I would be mistaken in assuming that you might have spent a little time in the gym since we saw you last year?

Your dyed hair also meets with huge approval amongst me and my friends! And I must say that I am delighted about your recent decision to stop wearing those dresses with huge lapels that you seemed so very fond of...

While I am writing this, it occurs to me to mention that I live reasonably nearby in a small but comfortable flat in Wandsworth. It's not such a nice area as Wimbledon but I was thinking that since you're bound to be at the tournament next week, well, I thought that perhaps you might like to drop in one day. I have put my phone number at the top of this letter so do feel free to call me any time. I sometimes go to bed quite early, but I really wouldn't mind if you called very late or very early... or really any time you wanted.

I don't want you to think me in any way presumptuous but I feel that we might have quite a bit in common. I know that on the surface it might not appear so. You after all are from Czechoslovakia (though I don't mean to dredge up any bad memories for you by mentioning that) and you're an internationally esteemed sportswoman and I am at present working as a care assistant in Balham, but these facts aside, I think that we might have some good talks together were we to meet up.

If however you are too busy and we do not get the chance to see each other this year, then I would like to wish you all the very best of British luck with the tournament (and by saying that, I am assuming that Jo Durie will pose no serious threat to you this year) and I hope that your career goes from strength to strength.

Yours sincerely,
Clare Summerskill

PS: I have just been chatting to someone sitting next to me who has just mentioned that they rescheduled your match earlier today and that you've already played it out on Court Fourteen while I was watching the men. I don't know the result but if I get the bus now, I might get home in time to see the highlights... no pun intended.

*(Clare rushes off stage with her umbrella open.)*

# SALAD DAYS

*Set in a student room in a hall of residence.*

God, that was fantastic! Wow! That was something else. Damn, we've been lying on my essay. I can't hand this in now – look, it's damp. I think that was me. Oh, what the hell, it was worth it.

I feel I should tell you something, though: that was my first time with a woman. No, I've never actually done it before! But it just felt so right, didn't it? So natural. When we kissed, it was so much nicer than with a man, wasn't it? Much softer. I'd really love to show you some poems I wrote when I was at school.

Do you smoke?

Oh good, I've got some really good stuff.

*(Clare starts rolling a joint with Rizla papers.)*

God, that was so good! Do you think anyone heard? I was quite loud, wasn't I? And these campus walls are like paper, aren't they? I mean, I know 'cos there's this American exchange student in the next room called Hank and he had a girl with him the other night and they were making so much noise, so everyone who lives in the corridor was standing outside his room giggling and when he came, we all applauded and cheered. It was hysterical!

Sorry, I shouldn't use that word, should I? Hysterical. Well, it was one that came up in the Women's Group meeting last week about male oppression of the womb in language. They're usually quite good, but sometimes the women who run them don't seem very happy – you know, considering how liberated they are. Like, when you go past the Women's Room, you know, in the Student Union, and there's always someone crying, isn't there? And another woman hugging her.

But on the whole, the Women's Group meetings are better than the Lesbian and Gay Soc ones. They're always about whether bisexuals should be able to join or whether they should have their own society, so it can get a bit boring. But I was so terrified the first time I went to one, 'cos I thought some big hairy bulldyke would leap on me after the meeting. No such luck!

*(Lots of giggles.)*

God! I still can't believe what I've just done. And with you!

You know when we occupied the science block last term? Do you remember me from then? 'Cos we slept in the same lecture theatre, didn't we? And I thought you were gorgeous. I've had fantasies about you ever since. I shouldn't be telling you this, should I? Well I did, and I didn't even know you were gay.

You weren't? I'm your first too? God! That's incredible!

*(Brief pause as Clare continues trying to roll a spliff, and continues to fail miserably.)*

Have you been down to Greenham yet? I have. I went with a friend and we took our guitars and sang political songs there. Well, they were mostly Joan Baez numbers about illegal immigrants coming over the Mexican border, but it's all the same sort of thing, isn't it?

Have you been to that political bookshop where they sell lesbian records in the back? They're fantastic! I've bought three already. Have you heard of Lesbian Concentrate? No, I am being serious. It's all these dyke songs and poems by different women. Wait a minute. I'll play you some if you like...

The bathroom? It's just down the corridor on the left.

*(Clare puts a very oddly shaped joint in her mouth which immediately falls apart.)*

## BRAND NEW GIRLFRIEND

I've got a brand new girlfriend –
You'll meet her one fine day –
But don't go using the "L" word
'Cos she doesn't like to think of herself as gay.
She says I'm the first woman she's ever loved
And basically she's really straight,
But I'm sure we can get it all sorted
'Cos I'm in love... And love is great!

I've got a brand new girlfriend –
You'll love her, she's a riot –
But keep it underneath your hat
Because she hasn't told her girlfriend so we have to keep it quiet.
She's going to tell her soon now
But she's waiting till the time is just right,
Which means she's sensitive as well as thoughtful
And I'm in love... And love is out of sight!

I've got a brand new girlfriend –
She's sweeter than a honeycomb –
But you'd better come round and meet her soon
'Cos if she doesn't get a visa then she has to go home.
I've never been to Greenland,
But just how hard can that language be?
I'm sure we can get it all sorted
'Cos I'm in love... And love will set you free!

I've had my share of disappointments
But it hasn't ever stopped me yet.
I have to keep on searching –
I'm convinced there's someone made for me I haven't yet
    met.


I've got a brand new girlfriend –
I've a feeling this is going to be great –
I can't see any problems
With caring for three children who are all under eight.
And I love it that she's religious,
But her church doesn't know she's gay,
But I'm sure we can get things sorted
'Cos I'm in love... so let's all pray!

I've got a brand new girlfriend –
She's sexy and she's kind –
I see her every day now,
But therapy's expensive when you're going all the time.
I know she's seeing other women,
But they all look so forlorn.
I'm the only one who comes out grinning,
I'm so in love... and overdrawn!

I've got a brand new girlfriend –
She just doesn't know it yet.
It's someone that I work with –
And I don't know what she's called because we haven't yet met.
But I found out where she's living
'Cos I followed her home one night
And she called the police and got me arrested,
But I'm in love... And love's all right!

I've had my share of disappointments
But it hasn't ever stopped me yet.
I have to keep on searching –
I'm convinced there's someone made for me I haven't yet
    met.

I'm clean out of girlfriends –
I've slept with everyone I know.
It all ends in disaster
And I'm left there feeling stupid and I've nothing to show.
I've found love don't come easy
When you're looking for your perfect Miss Right.
Now would someone please release me
From falling in love... 'Cos love is shite!

# BARBARA

Hello there, girls, my name's Barbara, or Babs, as everyone calls me. I live in a little village in a beautiful sixteenth-century cottage, wattle and daub walls, that sort of thing, inglenook fireplaces, huge kitchen, four bedrooms, lovely little garden at the back and I grow all my own vegetables. Used to share it all with the ex but she's gone off now with somebody else. These things happen, no point dwelling. Doesn't help of course that she's living in the next bloody village with her latest floozy, who I introduced her to. Yes. She was a friend of mine. Not any more. I'm not usually the sort of person to bear a grudge, but damn difficult to pass the time of day with someone who's gone off with the wife, so to speak. Anyway, onwards and upwards, that's what I say!

I must admit that after Daphne left me I did feel a tiny bit sorry for myself. But no point moping around, is there? It's just that we used to do everything together and it's odd, not knowing that she's off somewhere in another room. And we used to have quite a few visitors over, in the old days, but I don't really feel the urge so much now for that sort of thing. I remember once we had some girls up from London for the weekend and we all went down to the local pub and got rip-roaring drunk and came back through the village at closing time with all of us singing at the top of our voices: "We are family: I've got all my sisters with me!" Well, at choir practice the next morning none of the other villagers said a thing but I'm jolly sure they knew it was us. Oh yes, I used to go to church with Daphne as well. We were called the "spinsters of the village" – with affection, I think. But I don't really go along any more, to church or to the choir, because, well, I know that she'll be there, and it doesn't do to make waves, does it?

But there's still plenty of other things to keep me busy these days. Recycling, for one. I've got the old compost crock in the kitchen. Then there's paper, card and plastics. Now, none of that's collected kerbside, because it's bulky, so you have to take it along to a recycling skip. And, all in all, it's a very time-consuming thing to keep on top of, and it can actually take up most of the day if you are really following all the instructions to the letter.

But all this recycling business has actually given me a little idea which I've been working on. You see, since Daphne left and I've been feeling a teeny bit on the glum side, as I mentioned, mustn't grumble, people far worse off in Liverpool... I've realised that I've got quite a few other friends like myself, of the "lebanese" persuasion, who have all lost their partners, one way or another. Makes us sound like a careless lot, when I put it that way. But here we are, all single now, none of us fancy each other but we're all looking for company; and I wondered if it wouldn't be possible to come up with a sort of recycling scheme for girlfriends? Because it seems a shame that we've all been sort of discarded and aren't being used any more, when there's still quite a bit of life left in us, so to speak. Well, except maybe for my old friend Emma from Lower Keesdon, who is now so bitter that I think maybe she's best left on the scrap heap. But as for all my other friends, I think it would be a splendid idea!

Not sure exactly how it would work – still thinking it through. Maybe along the lines of gathering all the girls up on the village green, next to the bins, and then separating the women into categories: those wanting a long-term, into-the-sunset relationship by one bin, those needing someone just to be a little interested in them for a short while because they've lost all their confidence after their girlfriend did the dirty on them, those just wanting a bit of slap and tickle, no strings attached, and those who aren't particularly interested in doing anything under the sheets and just want a like-minded person with whom they can happily listen along to *The Archers*. And then we'd have to have some sort of village fair thing, where other "lebanese" women knew about the event and were all invited along and they could have a look at what was on offer and make their selection and that way all these lovely, lonely women wouldn't go to waste.

Just a thought. And I'll leave you with another one before I go: one recycled tin can save enough energy to power a television for three hours. Jolly good! Cheerio!

## ANGE: LADY IN RED

Hello. Ange again. As well as being a publican, I'm also a music lover. Oh yes. And may I just say at this point that I think that that particular song, "Lady in Red", is one of the finest melodies ever written in the English language. Because, as well as being a good old toe-tapper, it's a romantic number too, isn't it? And when you listen to it, there's probably a certain someone that you've got in your mind. Your very own Lady in Red, if you know what I mean. And I can tell by those nods that a few of you do.

And yes, I must admit that for me it brings to mind a certain incident with a certain "lady". In fact, I think that little Chris De Burgh might well have been a fly on the wall in my pub, except of course that it's a women-only establishment... with gay men welcome as guests, but I don't think Chris is that way inclined, is he? Anyway, the point being that the song actually reflected the events of that evening.

It was a quiet Monday night when she walked in, my very own "Lady in Red". She was what you'd call a stunner. Filmstar looks. I'm not exaggerating, she could have been a model. Very glamorous. And we don't have a lot of them walk in the place looking like that. Well, not the women, anyway. So I noticed her straight off. And after I'd served her a drink, I started chatting with her a little bit, 'cos she was on her own and I like to be friendly, especially to the newcomers. And all I said to her was, "What's a lovely lady like you doing in a place like this?" and suddenly her eyes filled up with tears and she started crying, so I gave her my handkerchief. Luckily it was a clean one. Then I asked Vicki at the bar to keep an eye on things while I took the young lady over to a quiet table, and that's when it all came out.

She'd had a row with her husband, hadn't she? They lived nearby

74

and she'd run out in a state and popped in to the nearest pub for a quiet drink, not realising... you know. Well, I didn't mind, if she didn't. And put it this way, she didn't seem to. She told me all about him. The husband. Sounded like an absolute so-and-so.

When she finished her story, she said, "Thanks for the handkerchief."

So I says, "Anytime. You can keep it if you like."

And then she goes, "Can I ask you something?" So I goes, "Yeah," and she says, "Do you mind if just sit here next to you for a bit because somehow you make me feel safe?" So I says, "Yes, of course."

And you know what? That's exactly what she did. And we just sat like that, no funny business, with her head resting on my shoulder for nearly twenty minutes, I'd say. In complete silence. But during that time we had a sort of connection. You know what I mean. I could feel it. And then this song, "Lady in Red", comes on the jukebox and suddenly she goes, "Would you dance with me?" And so I did. No-one else was dancing. The other girls were playing pool so it was just the two of us and I got some funny looks from Vicki, I can tell you! But I didn't care 'cos it was a very special moment. And I don't say this about a lot of women but this one was truly beautiful. I mean it. A true beauty she was. Yeah.

And then the music comes to an end. And she goes to me, "Thank you." Then she gives me a kiss on the cheek, she goes out the door and she leaves. Just like that. And I haven't seen her since.

But that song, "Lady in Red", that always reminds me of her. You know where it goes: "I've never seen so many men want to be there by your side." (Well, I change that bit to women, you know, in my head.) "I've never seen so many women want to be there by your side..." ('cos it does fit if you sing it that way, doesn't it?) "and when you turned to me and smiled, you took my breath away." And so on and so forth.

Well, I expect you know the rest of the words. Most people do, don't they? So yes, that's who I'm thinking of when I hear that song, and do you know what? I never even knew her name. Now, if that isn't a romantic story, then what is? So I know I might look a bit frightening to some of you, what with my leather trousers and my tattoos, but I expect that you can tell that deep down, me, well, I'm just a big softy, I am!

# LUCY: IN A TRANCE

Hi again, remember me? Lucy – but some people just call me "Loose". Get it! Well, not everyone, but like Nina, she called me that last week, like as a joke. Well, not completely as a joke because in fact I'd got off with someone that she was sort of involved with at the time, who was in actual fact her girlfriend. But I didn't know that and the other girl, well, she like forgot to mention it to me, and I'm not psychic, am I?

But if you want advice on relationships, well, I suppose I'm the one to ask. My last relationship was... on Tuesday. 'Cos I mean, like personally, I think life's too short to get all involved with just one girl. 'Cos like usually, by the second or third time I've done it with someone, lesbians start getting all serious and like, asking all these heavy-duty questions, like where do I live and stuff like that, or else they might, like, decide to dump me, in which case it's better to try and get in there first.

I mean like, the other night, I was in the Sweetie Wrapper Bar, right, and there was this girl, right, and she was well fit and we were, like, looking at each other and then, like, pretending that we weren't and next thing I knew she'd come over, right, and asked me for my mobile phone number. I mean, what a cheek! So I gave it to her and then five minutes later she only goes and bluetoothed me her contact details with a photo and all. No, I'm serious, and let me tell you, she was a babe! And she said her name was Natalia, right. And I thought that was really cool that she trusted me with that sort of personal information so early on in our relationship.

So we got talking and decided to go on to this clubnight which was on, which was sort of techno, trance, house sort of vibe. It was like amazing and Nina was there and I knew she had some gear on her but I didn't know if she was still mad at me about her girlfriend, who I went with, who I didn't know was her girlfriend – no-one tells me anything.

So I went up to her to ask anyway and she said it was cool and so I scored some stuff off her for me and Natalia, right, and we took half a tab each, right, and after a while we were really, like, really connecting, you know what I mean. And there were all these cartoon characters projected over the wall, like Popeye and stuff and it was well wicked and I couldn't stop dancing, 'cos you can't, when you're on that stuff, can you? And we were really out of it. And Natalia was looking so gorgeous, and I had to keep touching her and stroking her, 'cos you do when you're on that stuff, don't you?

And then like about six o'clock in the morning we were so wide awake and we were asked to this party, and only the really cool and beautiful people were being asked. Well, I wasn't asked directly, but Natalia was and she said I could go along with her. So we went along to this really brilliant chillout party and there were lava lamps and stuff everywhere and then Natalia disappeared for absolutely ages and I was getting really paraonid, 'cos you do when you're on that stuff, don't you? And eventually she came back and she said that she'd been talking to this other girl who told her that the stuff I'd bought off Nina was in actual fact an Anadin tablet.

And when she told me that, I was well vexed and I said to Natalia that maybe we should try and prosecute Nina under the trade description act or something and Natalia said she thought I was talking shite and that anyway she had to go home 'cos she suddenly felt really tired and get some sleep 'cos she had to go to work in a couple of hours. 'Cos she's like a pilot or something. So then I said, "Well, I didn't fancy you anyway, you're dumped."

Well, I didn't have any work on that day, 'cos, like, I'm freelance in what I do, 'cos I work in the IT, technology, computer, website, iPod sort of world and it's sort of flexi hours. Well, I'm sort of between jobs at the moment. But the thing is, I needed to get back home in time to catch *Trisha*, which is not my girlfriend but is in fact the show on TV, which is really good. So I got on the bus, right, and I fell asleep and missed my stop and ended up at the bus depot and had to get another bu`s to get home and then I fell asleep and missed it again. But I did manage to get back in time for *Neighbours*, not the lunchtime one, the early evening edition, and then I had to get myself sorted so I could to go to the Sweetie Wrapper Bar again that evening so I could try and get off with someone else. I was really hoping that Natalia wouldn't be there, but even if I do bump into her I'm not going to let it stop me having a good time 'cos that's what it's all about, isn't it, having a good time?

Right, I've got to go now, see you later, check it out, keep it real.

# CAROLINE

You're not from the press, are you? No? I don't just talk to anyone, you see, I have to be quite careful in my line of work. Makes me sound like a spy, doesn't it? No, actually, I'm in television. You've probably seen me doing this or that. If I said "Antiques" to you? Yes, I think you're there, aren't you? No, you're not? Well not everyone watches daytime television.

But I'm not actually "out" at work you see. I'm not "closeted", no, it's just that in my particular profession, the media, you can't really go around saying that you're gay. Well, obviously, the boys can, but for us gay women – and I'm sorry but I'm not going to call myself a "lesbian" because I don't like that word – for gay women, it's not so easy. So, anyway, at work, mum's the word. Not that I'm "out" to her either, of course. My mother. Well, you haven't met her! She'd have an absolute fit if she knew. She still invites eligible young men over for tea whenever I'm home. Sometimes I'm stuck with them for hours. Daddy might not mind so much, if I told him. He just wants me to be happy. But it's probably best if I don't say anything. It's easier all round that way.

So no, they don't know about Susie either. Sorry. She's my girlfriend. She's in television too. No, not a presenter. She's in sound. Holds the furry thing up in the air. Well, she says it's far more complicated than that. But that's how we met.

We don't really go out together much. Not on the "scene" anyway. We went to a men's bar once with some friends of ours. Lovely boys. On the whole I feel much more comfortable with gay men than I would with, well, you know, those "dyke type" women you sometimes see. Why do they have to look that way? Do you know, when I see those sort of women, I always think to myself, "How can they possibly manage without a handbag?"

Susie's a little younger than me and says she'd quite like to go to a gay women's bar or club one day (you see, I was her first!) but of course the main thing is that if I did go to somewhere like that, all evening I would just be absolutely terrified of being recognised. So we might as well just stay at home and watch the video of *Desert Hearts* again. It's easier all round that way.

And it's not as if I don't *have* a social life. God no! I'm out all the time. I mean, there's endless auctions and lunches and then there's charity balls and media parties. And it does help to be seen, you know, in my line of work. And Susie is so sweet about it all. She drives me there and takes me home afterwards. It's not that I don't want her with me. No, it's just easier if I don't have to explain who she is. And besides, she says she wouldn't have any of the right things to wear. You see, she's quite... how shall I put it? Well, "boyish" looking. Not in a "male" way, of course, no, she's very pretty. In a "Peter Pan" sort of way. You'll see her later, she's coming to pick me up. But you mustn't be put off by the beard. It's just a false one she puts on when she's doing her "chauffeur" bit. And I sit in the back seat. You know, so there's no gossiping. I mean, the papers can be vicious, can't they? So we just don't give them the opportunity.

But don't get me wrong. I'm not ashamed of anything and I'm quite happy to be who I am and all that. I just don't feel the need to broadcast it to the world. And, to be perfectly honest, it's easier all round, that way.

# AVRIL

*Avril has a strong northern accent and is wearing a tracksuit.*

Hello, my name's Avril. I'm originally from Lancashire, but I think I've lost most of my accent since I've been living in the south. I trained at Bedford PE college and I've been a games teacher ever since. And if you want my advice on how to get yourself a girlfriend, forget about all this going out and meeting total strangers you've got nothing in common with. No, you want to take up some form of sport. Me, I'm head of the games department at my school and I love my job, and I love the kids, but mainly I just love doing sport all the time. It's really great because, well, I suppose you could say, "Me, I'm sport mad, I am."

And where I work there are some good perks to the job. "Free use of tennis courts and swimming pool" in the holidays is a bonus, but the best thing is that I can more or less choose who I have working for me in my department. And as it happens, her name's Kim and she's very nice and she's sport mad too, she is. And she's under me, so to speak and yes, I think you've already guessed that we're what you might call an item. Didn't take very long for that to happen 'cos, well to be honest, as soon as I saw her in the interview, I fancied her. So I gave her the job and asked her out the day she started work. So we're both at the school together and as of last weekend, we're living together as well. And that was a really big decision which we thought about for quite a long time, but after a couple of weeks we decided "Oh, what the heck!" because we really get on and of course we have a lot in common 'cos, well, we're both sport mad, we are.

And Kim plays for the local women's netball team – that's on a Saturday – and there's a good chance that she'll be picked for the regionals next year. Fingers crossed. But it's very competitive, netball, and you do get some quite aggressive women playing it, from what I've seen. And in Kim's team it's all a bit incestuous as well 'cos, like, the goal attack, she goes out with the centre who's an ex of the wing defence *and* the goal shooter, so things can sometimes get a little heated, on and off the court.

But my main thing is golf, which Kim says isn't really a sport at all, but I think she's just winding me up. At least the women I play with haven't all slept with each other. Well, having said that, the team captain does go out with one other woman on the team, and most of the other women are gay, but there's not all that tension like Kim has with her netball.

Kim says golf's for when you retire and you wouldn't get her playing it and she says she can never understand what I'm talking about when I come back from a match. Says it's all gibberish. But I think she could follow if she paid a little more attention. I mean, for example, last Sunday, I came home and was talking about my opponent and all I said was that she was playing off twelve so I had to give her one on the fourth, took my five iron, sliced it into the semi, but I knew with a slight fade with a nine I should be able to knock it stiff. Even with a bogy I'd go one up.

Now, what's not to understand about that?

But one day I'll get Kim to try golf, 'cos I think she'd be very good at it and then we could do it together 'cos, after all, she is sport mad, she is. And it's nice to have things in common with your girlfriend. I mean, my ex, she was a bus driver and she wasn't into sport at all. So after a while I decided to knock it on the head, but she wasn't too happy about that. In fact, she turned up one night at the school when I was having a parents' evening there and she burst into the hall, saw me and started shouting in front of everyone that she still loved me and would I have her back?

Well, the headmistress was very understanding about the whole incident and, between you and me, I think she's one of us too. But you have to be a bit careful in schools, don't you? Like, one time, this girl in a class, she says to me, "Miss, are you a lesbian?" So I says, "Why, do you fancy me?" Well, that shut her up!

But no, it's working out very well with Kim, because we've so much in common. So I think we'll probably be together for quite a while, 'cos, well, we're just sport mad, we are!

# THE EX FACTOR

When falling for a lesbian you must check out her ex:
Do they see each other all the time and swear there is no sex
And if you ever question it they say that they're just friends?
But can you really draw a line where friendship starts and loving
    ends?

"We've got so much in common," you've been told, but do you
    trust
Your lover not to weaken in a moment of pure lust?
I'm not a jealous person on the whole but now I find
That when it comes to lovers' exes I've a small, suspicious mind.

I wonder why my girlfriend has a best friend who is now an ex;
I wonder if they somehow still are lovers but without the sex.

I wonder if I'm getting in the way and interrupting the flow;
I wonder if it wouldn't be more sensible to pack up and go.

They're always on the phone together, "catching up," they say.
I can't believe they find so much to talk about each day.
A quiet romantic evening and the ex arrives in tears,
Then they go upstairs to chat about it, compounding all my fears.

When I finish with a lover, well, I won't see her again
'Cos I've better things to do than passing time with an old flame,
But other girls just can't let go and want to stay in touch
And the exes who are friends now are the ones I loathe so much.

I can't help thinking, "Is it only me that this behaviour appals?"
I can't help thinking why they ever finished with each other at all.

I can't help thinking, "Three's a crowd when it comes down to
    intimacy."
I can't help thinking, "Straights would never stand for this, so
    why should we?"

# GOING DUTCH IN LESBOS

I have noticed that, as lesbians, we don't often smile at each other in recognition of our shared Sapphic persuasions. In fact, we tend to glance down when passing a couple of obvious dykes who probably look more like us than we would care to admit.

On the early morning flight to Lesbos, there were, it must be said, quite a few of us in the terminal who looked a little alike. Thankfully, though, no-one I'd slept with (apart from my girlfriend, of course) – which always helps me relax a little at the beginning of a holiday. When we finally boarded the plane, I struggled along the aisle with my bulky backpack, banging into a few tutting passengers who had already found their seats. It wasn't really necessary to double-check that you were on a flight to the island of Lesbos, because at the point when the air hostesses asked over the Tannoy for anyone who required a vegetarian meal, more than two thirds of the passengers raised their hands. By the time the almost inedible food arrived, I had started to unwind just a weeny bit, but I was still tired and tense. The four a.m. start had completely done me in, but I told myself that once we reached our destination, I would go skinny-dipping in the wonderfully warm Mediterranean water, before indulging in a supper of local fresh fish and Greek salad.

The way to reach the small village where we would be staying was to ask two other dykes you had never met before if they wanted to share the exorbitant fare for a taxi. Then the four of you and a Greek taxi driver would all take your lives in your hands for a couple of hours through mountainous terrain, over unmade roads and round hairpin bends. This dangerous journey would finally bring you to the more secluded part of the island, avoided by most of the straight tourists, that was the lesbian resort of Skala Eressos. It certainly took quite an effort to find, but no-one ever said it was going to be easy to be blessed with a different sexuality from most of the population.

It had been my girlfriend's idea that I celebrate my big Four-O on holiday, and then I had the idea of asking some of our friends along too. We wouldn't all need to go around together; just a few disparate dykey singles and couples, staying in the same resort over the same period and maybe having a bit of a knees-up on the special day. I didn't know till we touched down at Mytilene and a warm blast of air hit me as I came off the plane, just how much I needed a holiday. And I didn't know till Jenny and I laid down our towels on the beach, just how much we needed to spend this time together.

It was only six months since we had been on the brink of splitting up. Jenny had told me she was seeing somebody and I remembered all those evenings when she had called me and said she was working late. And I'd fallen for it, every time, because I'm like that. Or I was like that. I was completely gullible about everything. Jenny could have told me Martina was on her train home and I would have asked if Pam Shriver was anywhere to be seen in the vicinity. But not any more. I'm harder now. Not so trusting. We stayed together, but it's not the same.

I still love Jenny. Hated her for quite a while, but never stopped loving her too, if that makes any sense. It had all come out one night when she said we needed to talk. I knew then, by that very phrase "We need to talk". Because those words never just mean, "We need to talk", do they? Because we talk all the time. Every day, as a couple, every evening, we talk, and we don't say that "we need to talk" before we discuss the shopping or our plans for the weekend. No, in my experience, "We need to talk" only means one thing. That your girlfriend is thinking of dumping you.

So, apparently we "needed to talk" and we did so. She told me all about this woman she worked with called Annabelle. That was her name. Still is, I assume. Jenny said it had all just been a bit of fun at first but that she had started falling for Annabelle and Annabelle had a girlfriend as well but wanted to keep her and go back to her and didn't want to become a couple with Jenny. You might have noticed from the little I've told you that I didn't even figure in these calculations. I was just the one Jenny went back to after it all went pear-shaped. You might also have thought that Jenny didn't actually need to tell me anything at all and that she was only mentioning it out of decency and respect for me and for our relationship, but you would have thought wrong. She told me because I had found her out. One weekend there was a phone call at our flat. I picked up the phone in one room at exactly the same time as Jenny and, before I could say anything, a voice went, "Jenny, is that you?" And Jenny said, "Yes, darling, but if you hear a click then Clare's picked up the phone, so be quick." And then, for the first time ever, I perversely enjoyed hearing another woman use that well-worn phrase, "We need to talk."

I think the thing that puts a lot of couples off splitting up is not so much that they couldn't live without each other, but what a drag it would be to start looking for another girlfriend. At a certain point, when things are going wrong with your lover, you sometimes think, "I really haven't got the energy to start again with someone new." Because it would involve going out at night to try and meet someone, and then I'd have to video *Coronation Street*, which is really good at the moment, and then I'd have to go on public transport if I met someone for a drink. And I'd have to drink, 'cos I couldn't do all that dating thing stone-cold sober. And then they'd only know me when I was drunk and loud and fun and they wouldn't like the other side of me when things settled down, the side that likes watching taped videos of *Coronation Street* when I've been out for the evening. I just couldn't face all that. It's so much easier to just stay with my girlfriend. Even if she has cheated on me, even if she has lied time after time to me, even if I can't trust her further than I could throw her... but dating a complete stranger? That sounds so horrendous. No, I might as well just stay with Jenny.

So we stayed together. We "worked it through" as best we could. I said I would never trust her again. She said she was so sorry she'd hurt me. I said I didn't want to leave her because no-one else laughed at my jokes. She said that's 'cos they weren't very funny, but she loved me so much she wanted me to think they were. I took a while to work out whether that was a nice thing of her to say or not, by which time she'd made me a lovely cup of tea and produced a large Galaxy bar and then we snuggled up together on the sofa and she stroked my hair and told me how stupid she'd been, would I ever forgive her and what time was *Ugly Betty* on? And it all felt so familiar and so warm and safe that I couldn't bear to give any of it up.

On that first day on the beach there were these women with a makeshift home-made kite, hand-knitted by the look of it, in true back-to-basic lesbian fashion. And we were watching them throw it up into the air again and again until it finally caught the breeze and took flight. Then the wind picked up and kept it flying confidently and in my mind's eye I saw what would happen if the woman holding it had let go. The string would have slipped through her fingers in a split second and the kite would have flown right away, up into the sky, way over the hills, into the distance, and they would never have found it again. And with that picture in my mind, I was so glad that Jenny and I hadn't let each other go. That we had held on. And whether it was Jenny or I who had done the holding, I wasn't sure, but at least we were together.

Karen and Stella were the first of our friends to join us in Eressos. They had told us approximately when they would be coming and we greeted them with welcoming hugs in the village square. We were then introduced to the strangers with whom they had shared a taxi. Owing to their proximity in the car and the vicious bends which had repeatedly forced them to lean on each other in a very un-English manner, they now regarded these two dykes as close and treasured travelling companions. After a cool drink in one of the bars and a quick discussion with someone from the travel agency, we helped our friends carry their luggage to the women's B&B where they would be staying.

Karen was a really old friend of Jenny's from her hockey days and I had always got on well with her, and Stella was a lot of fun too, so we made a good foursome. The day after that, two other couples arrived. Susan and Debs lived quite near us in London so we saw them often. We all met at a friend's dinner party but none of us had much time any more for the original friend, who was now dating a merchant banker and kept telling us how much money her girlfriend made and that she was still in the closet because, "Well, you guys just wouldn't understand, but it's a completely different world in the City."

Monica and Danielle also turned up at the resort. Monica is my best friend of twenty years (who is of course an ex-girlfriend, but so far back in the past that no girlfriend would ever think of feeling threatened, and the very thought of us ever having been together now makes us cringe and simultaneously go, "Ugh, no... yuk!"). Things might have been up and down with Jenny, but Monica had always been a rock to me and over the years had taken my side on absolutely everything, even over things where I can now see I might have been in the wrong. I loved her to bits, and smiled to myself at the thought that she had come along on this trip even though she couldn't think of anything more frightening than joining "a group of drunken, sunburnt, hormonally challenged lesbians from all over the world in very close proximity to each other".

So that was all the couples, and then there was Elena. Elena was an amazingly beautiful and talented singer who always declared that she was totally free and single and yet if you scratched a little beneath the surface you would always find that she was in truth seeing someone. Not the same someone as you had found out about before, a different someone. But it was always a mysterious someone and usually a very attractive someone of foreign descent. Elena arrived in Eressos on her own and I knew she wouldn't be able to remain alone for the duration. I looked forward to her trying to hide any romantic developments from me, telling me that nothing was happening and that she and the new someone she was clearly shagging were just good friends.

Over the first few days, the holiday seemed to be going well. We all agreed that we didn't always want to do everything as a group and that we were quite happy eating or drinking at separate bars and restaurants and meeting up if and when we felt like it. In spite of this agreement, we found ourselves generally joining the others every day on the beach, where we sat facing the sea and checking out the various shapes of all the other women around us. We were on the nudist part of the beach and there were all these lovely lady lesbian bodies playing volleyball, applying suntan lotion, running in and out of the sea. I know that politically speaking I should not admit to sexually objectifying other women, but I have to tell you that lying there and watching them all, my last remaining feminist credentials from the 1980s finally disappeared for good.

Inevitably, we bumped into women we knew from England. We hid from some behind sand dunes for long periods, but we were thrilled to see others and asked them along to my big party, to be held at the weekend. There was a lovely woman I knew called June, who was a doctor, and a lawyer friend of hers called Lucy. They came up to us as we were sitting on the beach and we chatted for quite a while – which was great except for the slight distraction of them being stark naked. I remember hoping that I would never require their professional services in the future because I just wouldn't be able to get that image out of my head, especially that of Doctor June who, as I recall, had a little string hanging out from between her legs.

One evening, a few of us ate at a restaurant with a couple from Holland whom Karen and Stella had befriended the night before. Nette and Angelica were both therapists. Angelica was dark and intense looking and clearly quite brainy and Nette was blonde and large and seemed the more fun of the two, but they both had a wicked sense of humour and laughed at the "alternative healing lesbian world of witchery and wonderment" that they happily inhabited. This reinforced my opinion that the only thing I really hate about the Dutch is their ability to speak English better than we do. But it didn't take long before we were looking out for them on the beach each morning and we would all sit together for yet another hard day of doing a marvellous impression of a group of beached whales stranded upon Sapphic sands.

Everyone seemed happy and relaxed... except for Susan and Debs, who were clearly going through a "tricky" stage. They could usually be found hanging out with the largest group available, presumably to avoid being with each other; or else they would go off together for long walks to the end of the beach, which took you as far as Sappho's Rock. This was not an island discotheque, as you might have feared from its name, but a dramatic and beautiful cliff leading down to the sea which, at the right angle, against the horizon, looked a little like the outline of a woman's body. But when Susan and Debs stormed off in that direction, you could see their arms flailing in heated discussion, before one of them would walk back on her own. They each knew better than to offload to us about how difficult and unreasonable the other was being, even though it was clear that they were both desperate to do so. So we never found out if all the tension was about one particular disagreement or whether this was just a couple who had been with each other too long and who had slowly but surely grown apart.

In the evenings they both drank far too much. They would not be seen on the beach till way after lunchtime, on account of their frightful hangovers. I cared for both of them – well, to be honest, I slightly fancied Debs, but it was literally a fancy. I wouldn't have wanted anything to come of it, but sometimes it's fun to have a little "twinkle" going on with a friend, isn't it? Or is that just me? But honestly, hand on heart, I wanted them to settle their differences and make up and be close again… and that way I could feel safer and happier about once again fancying Debs. But still the friction between them continued and Jenny and I didn't know what to do to help. And a selfish, unspoken part of us didn't want their fighting to mar our very special and badly needed holiday.

I can't flirt. I wish I could, but I've never been able to. If I really like someone, I find myself just taking the piss out of them a lot. That can, of course, be slightly misleading, but it's my misguided way of trying to amuse and impress. I can recall more than one conversation with a girlfriend who has said to me, "I was so sure you didn't like me when me met. I couldn't understand why you were being so mean!" But I'm also no good at being able to tell if and when anyone is flirting with me, which is partly how I got into trouble in Eressos that particular summer.

We were all down on the beach one day, a crowd of us having a good time – but when you're on holiday with friends in the sun you still manage to find things in life to complain about, so I was mentioning my bad back and saying that I'd had a rough night with it. The two Dutch lesbians immediately offered me a massage, yet another of their "alternative healing" skills. They briefly discussed who might be the one to perform the deed and decided upon Nette, who said she would come round to our studio early evening if I wanted, post-shower and pre-dinner, to give me a proper seeing to (my words, not hers!). This was one of the things I loved about this resort, because all around you would see women giving each other a haircut on the beach, or offering a little reiki to their mates. It was a bit like bartering – but even better, because I didn't have to give anything back – so I happily agreed to have Nette come round.

Jenny and I had rented a studio apartment in the village. It was owned and run by a lovely Greek woman called Joanna, who somehow managed to appear calm and friendly at all times, unfazed by the constantly changing variety of international lesbians coming in and out of her flats night and day. Dykes who were still at that totally "loved-up" stage, when they couldn't resist groping and kissing each other every second; dykes who had just had a terrible domestic but were totally oblivious to the icy aura they emanated; but also dykes who had been with each other for so many years that they could pack a joint bag for the beach without so much as a single word passing their lips – a level of achievement for which I have nothing but total admiration.

I was sitting peacefully on the balcony of our studio, sipping a cool lemonade and sheltering from the strength of the afternoon sun, when Nette called up to me from the road. Jenny was still on the beach. She usually stayed there till the sun went down, a real sun-worshipper, lapping up every single little ray. She'd always said that one day she was destined to live between the mountains and the sea. Neither country nor water mass was ever specified, and nor was the insignificant detail of whether or not I might be sharing that particular stage of her life.

I opened the door to Nette and she smiled warmly and asked where I would feel comfortable lying down: on the bed or the sofa? I thought the sofa would be best because it was narrower and would enable her to get round me from all angles. She told me to take everything off but my knickers; then, as I lay down with a towel around me, she gently lowered it down my back and began to work her fabulous finger magic. She had even brought some smelly oils to rub over me.

A happy little thing was I during that hour of personalised pampering and, by the time she finally announced that she was finished, I was lying on my back with my eyes closed and my mind drifting towards the realms of sleep.

"Thank you, that was so wonderful," I grunted.

She was standing behind me and said, "My pleasure," and then leant over and very gently kissed me on the forehead. Before I knew it, she had gone out through the door and I was left there, still with the towel over me, wondering if perhaps I had made the last bit up? No, she had leant over and kissed me. But what did it mean? That she liked me? That she fancied me? Or was it a special thing that Dutch women do at the end of a massage to show that it's finished?

"Would I tell Jenny?" That was the big question. "Well, of course not!" was my instant response. But if I thought that, then surely that meant there was something in it? So, if it wasn't to be made public, then it was to be a secret. Just between us: Nette and me. Oh my God! Something significant had just happened and I didn't quite know what it meant, but I knew it felt like fun. It seemed precious and exciting, but sweet and gentle and innocent at the same time – and I realised this was what I'd missed for so many years with Jenny. Feeling special, feeling cared for, feeling sought out from all the others in some small way. Not the sex – funnily enough, I could live without that – but the attention. Was that wrong? Was that needy? I didn't know. All I knew was that I wanted to stay there, lying on the sofa with that warm feeling running around my stomach and my brain, for a very long time, and not get up and not take a shower and certainly not go and find Jenny on the beach and tell her how much better my back was feeling and casually mention that the Dutch were a truly marvellous if sometimes underestimated race of people.

That evening, as a crowd of us sipped cocktails at the Sappho Hotel, I found myself waiting for a certain someone's arrival. I looked around expectantly as anyone either walked by the tables or sat down near us. Monica and Danielle had already joined us. Monica had an extremely bad case of sunburn and had been indoors all day, cursing the Mediterranean climate and wishing that she was holidaying somewhere sensible, like Iceland. Karen and Stella then pitched up. They told us all about the pony trek they had taken that afternoon, saying the animals were in such a sorry state that they had every intention of reporting the owners to the Greek equivalent of the RSPCA, if in fact one existed, and that their own backsides were so sore from a two-hour ride that they didn't think they would ever be able to walk properly again.

Elena then arrived with a gorgeous woman whom she introduced as her "friend Natalia" who was young, tall and glamorous and could easily have been a model. Quite what she was doing hanging out with a load of middle-aged English dykes bemoaning the shortfalls of a hot climate and a beautiful landscape was beyond me.

Some more people joined us and I looked up again in the hope that one of them might be my "certain someone", but it was just Debs. She caught my eager glance in her direction and mistook it for an enthusiastic welcome. She pulled a chair up close to tell me Susan was having a nap and would join us all later. Debs then started chatting away about how she felt so spiritually at home in Eressos. I was a little surprised because so far I'd only seen her sour-faced, angry, or drinking to avoid her sorrows. But I was pleased that she seemed to be getting something out of the holiday.

"I can't really explain it all," she began – but I had a feeling she would try and sure enough she continued: "There's just something about this place, things are coming up for me that I've never felt before and well, I just want to thank you so much for bringing me here."

It made it sound as if I had personally whisked her away, just the two of us, for a romantic honeymoon, so I quickly said: "Yes, Jenny has some great ideas sometimes!"

But she didn't seem to take the hint and went on: "It just awakens all your senses, doesn't it? The beauty, the peace, the hills, the sea. It makes me realise what I really want from life."

And at that point she started staring meaningfully into my eyes. I didn't like to ask her what on earth she was talking about, in case I might regret hearing the response. But that was a silly thought. She was probably just feeling a little lonely and sad that things weren't going well with Susan. She ordered a drink, gulped it down, ordered another and started gazing in an appreciative way at Elena's new girlfriend. That made me feel slightly safer, if a tiny bit irrationally jealous, but I quickly moved on from that and looked around, beyond the immediate company, to see if a "certain someone" was going to put in an appearance. I'm sure Jenny didn't notice that

I was distracted. She hadn't even asked me how the massage had gone and, as I watched her and Karen laughing their heads off about something, I realised that the days of my seeing Jenny through the eyes of a lover were unfortunately long gone and that, although I still cared for her deeply, it was with less of a lustful longing and more of the fondness of familiarity.

I was on my second piña colada before I noticed that Nette had joined the group with Angelica. I felt my tummy flip over inside me, a sensation I remember experiencing on a regular basis when I was fifteen and Miss Boxall would come into the classroom every morning to take registration. Nette caught my glance and her beaming smile combined with twinkling eyes convinced me that I hadn't been exaggerating the significance of what happened that afternoon. I think I went bright red – not an incredibly mature thing to do but I hoped anyone who'd seen would put it down to my drinking. I'm not teetotal by any means, but from years of holiday drinking experience I have trained myself never to have more than two cocktails a night. At thirty-nine, I had learnt that piña coladas might taste exactly like milkshakes but the way I behaved after having drunk a few proved they were not one and the same.

Jenny suggested to everyone that we try a certain seafood restaurant that was known for serving delicious sardines. I thought that sounded a little improbable as a concept, only ever having encountered a sardine before in a tin with brine, but I was prepared to be proved wrong. All the restaurants were along the main stretch of the village, looking out to sea. Jenny's choice was right at the other end from the bar where we were drinking, but a few of the women with us eagerly agreed to come along. Monica and Danielle jumped up, as well as Elena and her "just good friend, Natalia", and Debs said she would come too and leave Susan to find us all of her own accord if and when she regained consciousness. I noticed Debs had a spring in her step as she paid her bill and she laced her arm through mine as we began to walk towards the restaurant. I turned my head back to see if Nette was coming, but she remained at the table with Angelica and a couple from Paris, and I felt a little pang of disappointment.

I walked through the village with Debs chattering in my ear about how, like Phil Collins, she too could feel something "coming in the air tonight". I had always found Debs' flirty behaviour a lot of fun, but for the first time ever it seemed rather annoying and slightly childish. I tried to work out what on earth was happening to me. I knew that it felt exciting, this link that Nette and I had somehow forged, and I knew that nothing would come of it, because we were both with long-term partners, and that that was probably the best way it could be. But a little unattainable longing suits a lesbian just perfectly, doesn't it? Or at least, that had always been my experience. But could you keep it at that? Well, of course you could, if it really was someone unattainable, like Ellen Degeneres or Susan from *Neighbours*. But if it was a friend you liked... on holiday... from another country... whom you wouldn't see again... well, where would be the harm?

I didn't know the answer and by that time in my thought process we were all sitting down and it was my turn to order.

"Just enjoy it," I told myself. "Enjoy it all. This is all part of the fun, isn't it? A load of women in the middle of the Mediterranean. Of course a few sexy sparks are going to be flying around here and there, it's all part of the experience. Nothing to get stressed about. And at the end of the day, albeit a day full of fantastical imagination running a little wild, you've still got a lovely girlfriend to go back to, so either way you're laughing!"

Sometimes I so wish that I could learn to listen to the sensible part of me that gives the silly side of me such good advice.

The evening passed uneventfully. Susan managed to track down Debs by the time we were all onto ice creams and coffees. They sat together at the end of the table talking quietly and intensely until Debs moved places and plonked herself between Monica and Danielle. I walked back to the studio with Jenny, hand in hand. Before long she was doing that thing that far too many tourists do when enraptured by the charms of their holiday resort – and sure enough, out popped the inevitable question. No, not the one about whether we should get married, but the one about how much a place here would cost to buy.

"You really like it then?" I asked.

"It's all come together, hasn't it, with our friends and everything? I wasn't sure how that would work, but everyone's getting on, aren't they?"

"Yes, it's brilliant," I said.

"And whose clever and wonderful idea was all this then? I forget now," said Jenny. "Oh yes, it was mine, wasn't it?"

As well as being significantly more self-confident by nature, Jenny is also a far more sociable creature than I, which was part of the appeal all those years ago when we first met. I like people but I'm better at one-to-ones and talking about things I find really interesting or important rather than general chit-chat. Jenny loves a crowd, a gang, a group, she loves to belong, whereas deep down I'm probably more of a loner. But she was really enjoying the "village" life of Eressos, bumping into familiar faces left, right and centre, something that doesn't happen too often in Leytonstone. But village life can be a double-edged sword (if one were ever tempted to look at it in terms of a weapon of war). The upside being that everyone knows everyone... and the downside being that everyone knows everyone. And that was to prove my undoing.

The next day on the beach was slightly cloudy and chilly and at lunchtime Jenny and I left our compatriots huddled together in true "British at the seaside on a Bank Holiday" style and we wandered off to a café hut that sold Greek salads and drinks. Nette and Angelica, being sensible women and not British, were there already and Angelica asked me how the massage had gone. I said it was great and burbled something about having slept a lot better that night, which in actual fact wasn't the case since I'd had strange and troubled dreams about her girlfriend.

Jenny then asked Angelica if she had seen the little turtles in the pond by the beach, saying that they often came out when it was overcast or raining – and before we knew it, they'd both gone off to look at them.

There was a short silence after which Nette said: "So, you really feel the massage helped?"

"Yes, yes, it was great. Thank you. Really great. Thanks. Cheers. Yeah."

I'm not sure if completely losing the power of speech might have given away the fact that I was a teeny bit nervous. As I mentioned previously, I usually have no idea when people are flirting with me, but I began to pick up certain signals from Nette that made me think that was exactly what she was doing. She moved her chair a little closer and as she spoke she lowered her voice slightly and stared right into my eyes.

"Do you think you might enjoy another massage at some point?" she asked.

I wondered whether she had used the word "enjoy" deliberately, making it sound like a mistake any non-English speaker would use. And yet I happened to know that her English was better than mine, so why hadn't she just said, "Do you think you might like another massage?" OK, I was probably reading far too much into it all, and after my feeble attempt at sentence deconstruction I heard myself clumsily muttering something along the lines of, "Erm, yes, please, if you're not too busy, if you want to, that is, if Angelica doesn't mind at all..."

There now, I'd said it, if not actually spelt it out. I had admitted to her that I knew it was all looking a little bit suspicious, if anyone with a suspicious mind might be doing any looking. Nette, however, ignored the direction of my inquiry and with a beaming (and, it must be mentioned, rather cute) smile, said she would be happy to pop over to my studio again later that afternoon.

Intense excitement immediately clashed in my mind with several worrying thoughts. Would Jenny think it was dodgy if I told her I was having another massage? Would Angelica mind at all? Would either Jenny or Angelica have the slightest suspicion that anything other than a massage was going on? And far more importantly, what *was* going on? In my imagination I was already way past the massage. We had now kissed passionately and had wild and totally fulfilling sex and I had moved to Rotterdam to start a new life with Nette and was pondering the question of whether a Dutch lesbian audience would speak English well enough to understand my stand-up material, provided of course that I dropped any references to Amanda Burton.

But in reality, at this point Nette had only asked if I wanted another massage, albeit with a poignant glare that had pinned me into my chair and left me short of breath and unable to move. And then, as if in response to all my unspoken confusion, Nette said, "I am very attracted to you. You do know that don't you?" To which I replied with complete confidence and impressive eloquence: "Um, yes, well, you know, me too. I mean, not attracted to myself, that would be weird, but yes, to what you were saying."

And she was still doing that eye-contact thing where they don't blink or twitch or sneeze or anything but just stare deep deep into your soul and then I looked away from her gaze to see Angelica and Jenny bounding up to the table to join us. They started burbling on about the turtles being the sweetest little things you'd ever seen and Jenny was saying how they would do so much better in this sort of weather with a few umbrellas between them and then she was asking if it was in fact possible for a turtle to hold an umbrella with one foot or leg, or arm or whatever they had and not sink while they were doing so, in which case the umbrella selling idea might not be such a commercial opportunity in the turtle world after all.

And as the two of them were chatting away I felt that they could have been in a completely different time zone from me. I noticed that Nette was now joining in their jokes and it occurred to me that perhaps she had some previous experience of this sort of thing. The laughter, the instant change of mood seemed to come so easily to her. Was she just playing some sort of game? Because it wasn't a game to me – or if it was, I had no idea of any of the rules or even the language in which it was played.

Yes, I'd maybe sort of fancied a couple of women in the many years that I'd been with Jenny – Debs being one of them, as I mentioned, and Kirsty Wark from *Newsnight* being another (but I don't suppose she counts). But it had all seemed like a little bit of fun, something every dyke in a long-term relationship should be allowed to do once in a while, just to check that everything was still in working order! A bit like an MOT. But I had never felt this way before, the way I felt when I was around Nette. And it felt far more dangerous than fun, because if it ever got out of hand, it could seriously threaten my own relationship. But before I jumped ahead to examine that fear, the immediate million-dollar question was, "Did Nette feel the same way?"

As I watched her still chuckling away with the other two, I thought that I might have blown the whole thing out of proportion. But then again, she was the one who had said all that stuff about being attracted to me and I hadn't made that up, had I?

Someone settled the bill and in a daze I followed the others to our beach spots. Nette fleetingly turned her head round, without the others noticing, and winked at me. And with that one little crafty, sexy wink, I was hooked on her line and could do nothing else but wait until she decided to reel me in.

As it turned out, the second massage session never happened because Jenny had made an appointment for us to see the women who ran the Sappho Hotel, to discuss details about my birthday meal. Fortunately, Jenny took all the strain when it came to discussing the menu, drinks, music and seating arrangements and I just agreed and said that it all sounded wonderful, which was true. But my mind was elsewhere and I realised I was quickly learning to do something I had never done before with Jenny: to hide my innermost thoughts from her, hoping that a smile and a nod in the right place would suffice for communication and arouse no suspicion. I have, of course, over the years, been told that most people have lots of things going around their heads that they don't always let everyone else know about; but not me. It was only at this crucial point in my life that I realised there is another option: that of not speaking aloud every single thought you're thinking. Over the course of our relationship, Jenny had got used to my babbling on about what I thought of this or that, him or her, what I was going to do today and tomorrow and how my childhood injuries affected my current behaviour, outlook and personality. And in her wittier moments, as I chatted away, she would do a little mime of wiping blood from her ear, which meant that my incessant ramblings were making her ears bleed. Oh, how we laughed! But now I was thinking about something – all right, someone – almost non-stop for most of the day (and part of the night) and not saying one single thing out loud about my thoughts and feelings on the matter. And even more surprising than my learning to do this was that Jenny hadn't noticed anything. For someone who had known me for so long, it was strange that she appeared to have no awareness of this whatsoever.

That evening, we joined Monica and Danielle for a meal. I couldn't see Nette or Angelica anywhere – not at the restaurant nor at any of the bars – and my over-active imagination started picturing them having had an argument about me, and possibly splitting up and flying back to Holland. But the next morning they were there on the beach again, in their usual spot, all smiles, waving us over to join them. As cocktail hour approached, we packed up our things, showered and changed and all met up again at a bar to watch the sun setting magnificently on the horizon, like an aged actress making a glorious final curtain call. Again, the Dutch contingency were not to be seen but Debs had perched herself next to me and, as the final edge of the orange ball sunk away to obscurity behind the horizon, she put her hand on my arm and quietly said, "I need to talk to you."

"Oh, OK." I said, trying to replicate her serious tone. "Go on, then."

"Not here." She looked quickly around her as if in a scene from a film about the French Resistance. "Come for a walk with me."

"Erm, all right," I mumbled. "But won't that look a bit odd?"

"I really need to speak to you."

"OK, OK, I'm coming."

And with that I got up and told Jenny that Debs wanted to show me something in a shop that she'd had her eye on. Jenny barely registered my leaving but as we walked away I swear could feel Susan's eyes boring into the back of me. We set off in the direction of the shops but then Debs suddenly whisked me down a back street which came out onto a little track that led out of the village. When the sun sets in the Mediterranean it very quickly becomes dark and I could tell that without the village lights we would soon be walking along in total black. I pointed this fact out to Debs but she just replied, "It doesn't matter. I just need to be alone with you."

I decided to stop all this rambling, literal and metaphorical, and I said: "Right then, here we are, Debs, all alone. Now, what is it?"

Debs took my hand and pulled me down another smaller path, then drew a somewhat dramatic breath, paused meaningfully, sighed tragically and said, "You see the moon?"

We both looked up. Yes, it was still there in the sky, hadn't gone anywhere. "Yes," I replied, assuming this to be the correct response.

"And the stars..." Debs continued. "You see all the stars?"

"Yes," I said again, wondering if these were trick questions in any way, because so far they seemed rather on the easy side.

Debs went on, "I'm just finding that on this island I'm connecting to a sort of spirituality which is making me turn into a different person, and I know that I have you to thank for becoming that person and for bringing me here."

"Well, it was just a birthday party with knobs on really, nothing too mystical about that!" I was trying to lighten the tone but still had certain fears about where this conversation might be going.

"But it means that I've come here..."

"Yes," I said, "you and Susan..."

"And now I'm here with you."

"Yes," I battled on. "You and Susan and me... and Jenny," I added for good measure.

But still she persisted. "I'm trying to tell you something, but I don't know if you're hearing me?"

At this point what I really wanted to do was make a radio-noise sound-effect and go: "Cccch, I'm hearing you loud and clear, cccch!" But somehow I managed to restrain myself and actually said: "I am. You're saying that you like being here, with the moon and the stars and the spiritual feelings and..."

"And you," she added. "I think I'm in love with you."

Now, I am rarely accused of being a woman lost for words, but I hadn't the foggiest idea of what to say or even do after this revelation. Debs solved the problem for me by kissing me on the lips. In an embarrassingly fumbling way she then tried to prise my mouth open with her tongue. I, also imagining myself in a French Resistance film, firmly refused to let her do so, my jaws clenched together and my lips as tight as a baboon's backside.

The love scene Debs had imagined was clearly not going to plan. Yes, it's true that over the time we had known each other I had found her attractive, but I realised in that instant that it was only a fantasy. I didn't want this in real life and I couldn't go ahead with it, even though she obviously desired it quite stongly and even though the normal rules of behaviour seemed to have been thrown to the wind. But I just couldn't do this.

I wish I could say that it was courageous willpower and a sterling strength of character that held me back, but it wasn't. It was in large part a sudden lack of any physical interest in Debs and, to a lesser, but still significant degree, a worrying fear of what Susan might do to me physically if she were to find out. Susan, although clearly in a troubled relationship and somewhat vulnerable in that respect, was still, it must be said, quite a large girl who, it must be remembered, used to be in the police force, albeit working on the domestic violence side of things – preventing rather than performing I hasten to add but still, no sensible woman would knowingly set about to incur her wrath.

And yet, I knew even then that it was not just the fear, or even the fact that we might all lose each other's friendships. No more going out to the pictures in a jolly foursome followed by a pizza with anchovies, mozzarella and a heated debate about the film we'd all just seen. So, was it Jenny that was preventing me from taking this any further? My loyalty to her and to our relationship? Not wanting to deceive her any more than I already had? Yes, that must surely be the reason, I tried to convince myself. But deep down, I knew the truth. I didn't want to be here in a field in the dark with this woman coming on to me... I wanted to be in a field in the dark... with Nette.

Oh dear, this was getting complicated. I heard myself running off a load of excuses to doe-eyed Debs, as many excuses as I could possibly think of. I didn't want to ruin our friendship, which I really treasured. I didn't want to hurt or deceive Jenny. I wanted Debs and Susan to work out their problems and remain a couple because I thought they were so good together and I knew that if I got involved at this point it would be almost impossible for them to do that.

But still she pleaded with me: "Just one kiss, that's all I'm asking. Please, please. I've been wanting you for so long. I thought you felt the same way. I understand you, Clare, and I know this was meant to happen. I just feel it, it was fate that brought us here."

"Olympic Airlines, to be precise," I was thinking to myself, but let's not get too literal.

"Debs, it's not going to happen." I was trying so hard to sound firm but caring. I didn't want to hurt her, I really didn't. "I appreciate it so much, that you care for me and of course I'm flattered, but it would ruin everything and I just don't want to lose Jenny."

"Just one kiss, that's all I ask?" she pleaded.

"No, honestly, I really can't. "

She turned away but I could see that her face was full of hurt and anger and a part of me wanted to relent. To kiss her better, to make her happy again, happy and sexy and confident, like she'd been ten minutes ago. But I knew that it would be even more cruel to give her a little hope when there was none.

"Come on, let's go back now," I said, as gently as I could.

"You go," she replied. "I'm just going to stay here for a while."

"I'll wait then."

"No," she said sharply. "Just let me be alone. I need to get myself together."

"OK, if you're sure. Debs, I'm so sorry, I really am."

And, as I walked back to the village, I felt dreadful. It might sound corny but I really felt her pain and yet I knew it would have been wrong to have done anything with her.

But another reason I was feeling so bad was because I knew it was yet another thing that I was not going to be telling Jenny about – recalling the event over and over in my mind, wondering if I should have done or said anything different, but keeping it all a secret. By nature wanting to share my thoughts and feelings about it all with my girlfriend, but feeling that I shouldn't, that it would be unfair and slightly cruel to Debs to tell Jenny all about it.

Perhaps I could at least tell my best friend, Monica, about the whole thing. She would understand and I could count on her to be discreet. But on the other hand, I didn't want her to laugh too much at Debs making a bit of a fool of herself, because... well, let's be honest here, there but for the grace of God... And I knew I wouldn't be able to keep the element of humour out of the telling, so keeping it to myself was the only option.

But thinking about Monica made me examine the idea of letting her know what was going on with Nette. I couldn't predict how she might take that one. It's true that she's always been on my side in the past, but would she think that there was too much at stake to have a good old giggle about the whole thing? Would her morals maybe stand in the way and for the first time come between us in our friendship? The very thought was unbearable. But, in the process of mulling through all these possibilities, another image started forming itself in my imagination: a scene of what might have happened, had it been me and Nette together in that field in the dark, our girlfriends safely back in the village, with nothing but a weak and dismissible conscience to stand in the way of our desires.

The temperature had been rising again over the last couple of days and my actual birthday was another scorcher on the beach. Elena said it was so hot and close that it must be about to break any day now. I felt just the same way in my head. I spent the entire day doing what I enjoy most: sunbathing until I couldn't bear the heat any longer and then running into the water to cool down and repeating that all over and over again. Each time I was in the sea, I would be either swimming around or treading water, but my gaze was always fixed towards the part of the beach where Nette was sunbathing in the nude. She was fair-skinned by nature but managed to tan effortlessly to a beautiful golden brown. From the cool comfort of the sea, I could look at her for long periods without anyone noticing, feasting my eyes on that vision of delight. After each dip I would go back to my towel next to Jenny and – book in hand and eyes well hidden by sunglasses – lie on my left side and pretend to read. In fact, that position served to give me a good view of Nette while in no way betraying the fact that I was perving on her.

Debs and Susan came down to the beach after lunch and sat the other side of us. They put up a couple of parasols and when they settled down I caught Debs peering over her book to look at me while pretending not to. The whole situation was turning into something of an Ealing comedy. And there was Jenny, plopped down in the middle of all this, seemingly oblivious to everything. Then Nette and Angelica stopped by to chat to us and I was aware that three out of six of us were, to some degree, deceiving our girlfriends.

I felt myself torn between feeling guilt over Jenny, slight irritation at Debs' attentions and palpable excitement at the proximity of Nette's physical presence. And so the day continued until it was time to pack up our things and go back to our studio to get ready for the birthday meal.

Just before we went out to the restaurant, Jenny said she wanted to give me a present. She handed me a box which I unwrapped to reveal a jagged rock cluster. I didn't know the name of it but the inside was a beautiful purple colour. She knows I love that sort of thing and that, in spite of my occasional cynical comments about alternative lesbian lifestyles, I have been known to reveal tendencies to what she calls a "dippy hippy" side to my nature.

"Thank you so much," I said. "It's absolutely beautiful."

"There's a bigger present waiting for you at home, but it wouldn't have fitted on the plane."

"What is it? Tell me!"

"Can't tell you, it's a surprise."

"Well then, surprise me by telling me!"

"Well, you know you said you needed a new car..."

"You're kidding me?"

"Yes, I am!"

"Oh, ha ha! Have you really got me something else?

"Well, when we get home, I think you'll find that your office has been decorated by some friendly lesbian elves who I employed."

"Oh that's fantastic! I've been meaning to do that room for years."

"I know."

"And would these elves by any chance go by the names of Mary and Gill?" (Two lesbian decorator friends of ours.)

"When they finish their Christmas duties in the North Pole and appear in human form, those are indeed the names they go by."

"Oh thank you so much, darling." I kissed her on the cheek. "And for organising the party and the trip and everything."

"It's been fun. I wanted to... you know... try and make up a bit for... Well, wanted you to know how important you are to me and... and it's made me realise just how much I... I... need you."

And I was thinking: "Please don't say 'need', please say 'love'. Please let me know that I'm more to you than just a very close friend whom over the years you've grown to need. Please say that 'love' word so that I don't find myself looking elsewhere for attention to compensate. Please say it so I don't have to wait until a foreigner comes on to me on holiday and makes me feel like a woman once more, makes me feel desired and makes me feel desires that I never thought I'd feel again."

Being good friends with someone is fantastic and important, don't get me wrong, but there's no physicality involved, is there? A good friend doesn't notice if you've put on weight, or if you've dyed your hair, or if you're wearing a new top, but a lover will see these things, delight in them even, because she wants you to look good for her to enjoy. A lover will make you feel alive again in your body, not just in your mind. A lover will make your heart beat faster and the blood rush to your head in that moment when you receive a text with her name on it, just before you read it. A good friend is such a precious thing and to be valued and cherished dearly, but a good friend is not a lover.

I suddenly realised that Jenny was still talking. "And that I want you to know that I will always, always... care for you so very deeply."

She paused and I waited for more, but none came. She said nothing else about her feelings but simply led me out of the door, into the street and along to the restaurant.

It was a fantastic birthday meal. I counted eighteen women in our party. All our mates from England, Elena and her "good friend", Nette and Angelica, of course, and a couple of their French pals, the doctor and the lawyer and an Italian couple we'd met the day before who seemed really nice. Wine flowed, various courses arrived and the remains were cleared away.

Several times during the evening I looked down the table at Nette. Not too often and never for too long; wishing that I was sitting next to her, or at least opposite so we could play footsie under the table.

After dessert and coffee, I glanced over at her again, and that time she held my gaze and nodded. Two very subtle but nevertheless very discernible nods. God, this was horrible. How could anyone say that falling in love – or lust, or whatever the hell it was – was any fun? It was excruciatingly painful but, like a runaway train, impossible to halt once the wheels were in motion and the brakes disengaged.

Back on planet earth, I realised that a sound like a mosquito buzzing in my left ear was in fact Jenny saying something to me about how it was time to get up and make a speech. I didn't appreciate being wrenched so rudely out of my delicious daydream zone but, since I could in no way explain that to her, I consented and stood up to thank everyone for being there. I thanked them all for the lovely meal, the beautiful cards and all the presents I had received; and of course I thanked Jenny for organising the whole Lesbos Birthday Extravaganza. Everyone clapped and cheered and then Monica made a touching, if alcohol-fuelled, speech about how deeply she had loved me for so many years but how she just couldn't fancy me because I was now too old and she needed to be practical and think about how she needed someone younger like Danielle who had agreed to look after her in her dotage.

After she had finished, Jenny proposed a toast to me which everyone joined in. At that moment I felt overcome with something other that lust for possibly the first time that holiday. It was a sense of deep gratitude for all I had around me, this wonderful evening, my girlfriend and all my friends, my health and theirs. But the minute I realised what I did have in my life, I started thinking again of what I didn't have. What I still wanted. What, at that particular moment, I felt I needed more than anything else in the world. To go over to Nette and snog her so forcefully that she was left gasping for breath.

Of course, there was no way I could do that. I had to behave and must not do the one thing I ached for, the one thing that would have totally ruined this evening and possibly my whole life as I knew it. But once the image of such an act had entered my mind, I couldn't shift it for the rest of the evening.

After the last coffees had been sipped, most of the guests dispersed and the bill settled, Jenny asked me if I would mind her going off to bed. She had never been one for late nights and I said that was fine and, as casually as I could, mentioned that I'd maybe have another drink at one of the bars and then come up and join her. She kissed me on the cheek and I thanked her again.

"You deserve it," she said. "You're my little bear, aren't you?"

And we kissed again and then she went her way and I went mine. My way went directly to the bar where I knew Nette would be. As I approached it, the swarm of other women drinking there became a blur until I spotted Nette at the bar. She, by contrast, appeared in sharp focus. I assumed that Angelica had gone to bed too, since

Nette was alone, and I knew instinctively that she had been waiting for me.

"Hello, birthday girl," she said.

"Hello, you."

"Did you have a fun evening?"

"I couldn't bear not being close to you."

There, I'd said it. And then I started panicking. Was that too forward? Not nearly casual enough? Too heavy and inappropriate perhaps for the actual situation? But I heaved a sigh of relief as she said, "We can be close now. Come."

She took my hand and led me out of the bar, across the village square and towards the beach. For a fleeting moment, I worried if anyone might have seen us, but Nette gave me one of her "gaze into my eyes and you will never worry about anything again" looks, and after that I could think of nothing else – and before I knew it, there was just the two of us on the sand. Away from the lights of the village, we both sank down onto our knees and then came the moment for which I'd been longing and aching for so many days. It seemed like more than days, it seemed like a lifetime, and when we finally kissed, it was as if a need from the depths of my very being was at long last being met.

All the clichés, I know. But I can think of nothing original to describe that kiss, that instant, that sense of inherent pain being met by a long-awaited soothing touch of beauty. Everything about that moment was beautiful: Nette, the beach, the reflection of the moon shattering the water like glass, her hold, her touch, her mouth.

I couldn't pull myself away from her if my life depended on it and she knew the power that she held over me, and somehow that knowledge made it even stronger. Because I felt like I was being totally possessed, controlled, I had no choice or mind of my own – and that was how I wanted it. I couldn't think straight, I couldn't think at all. I just wanted to stay like this forever... being held, feeling safe, feeling loved and wanted and needed and with no choices to make ever again in my whole life.

The kiss finally ended and we stared into each other's eyes once more. We were holding hands and we concentrated on that for a while, changing our grip, turning each other's fingers over again and again as if that would somehow bring the answer to the question that was in both our minds: "Should we now go further?" Of course we wanted to and we could do it right there, on the beach, or we might go between the huts and then no-one could see us. All these possibilities were rushing around both our minds but no words needed to be spoken.

Nette led me gently by the hand and I followed her like a lamb to slaughter, desire clouding my ability to think this through, to look at the implications of what we were about to do. I paused for a moment, still holding her hand but looking back to the sea... and then once more into her eyes. Her hold over me was like a dangerous underwater current, close enough to the shore that no-one would suspect its power and yet strong enough to pull a grown woman into the depths of the ocean, fighting for her life.

As if she could sense my fear and hesitation, she held me close to her and kissed me again. In that split second I had an image of Jenny, and began to wonder what she would do if she found out, if this would break her heart the way she had torn mine apart a few months earlier. But I didn't want to hurt Jenny, I certainly wasn't doing it for that. And yet, if I was to carry on with this, she would inevitably find out and I would cause her a great deal of pain. So was it worth it? I tried to weigh up what I might gain and what I would lose if I followed Nette up the beach, but I was in no fit state to weigh anything up at all. I couldn't think straight. I really felt that I could not and should not go with Nette, but I didn't have the slightest ounce of strength in me to refuse her.

I felt her hand round the back of my neck as she drew my mouth once more to hers. I felt the waves crashing over me again, but just at that point, I suddenly pushed her away. She looked startled and took a step back from me.

"I thought you wanted to..." she said.

"I did, I do... but I can't. I just can't."

I slept very little that night. After running back to the studio, I climbed into bed next to Jenny and snuggled up against her warm body. I wasn't sure if she was awake or not and was slightly surprised when, after a few minutes, she said, "I'm so glad you came back."

If she felt my heart beating at a dangerously high rate, she said nothing about it and after a few minutes appeared to go off to sleep. I lay staring up at the white ceiling.

The lights from the road outside were enough to make me able to spot some black smudges on the paintwork where unsuspecting mosquitoes had clearly had their lives brutally cut short by a previous occupant wielding a newspaper. Daylight was appearing by the time I managed to drop off and then I slept right through till the early afternoon. Jenny had obviously gone down to the beach but had left me a little note saying she hoped I'd slept well and that she still loved me, even though I was now officially an "older lesbian".

There were two more days to go before our flight home. I could think of nothing else but Nette and what had happened – or rather what had not happened – between us. I longed to see her again but at the same time I was terrified of doing so, fearing that it was not in my power to refuse her advances more than once. But she was not at the beach nor around our usual bar that evening and a tiny part of me was relieved, since if she had been near me I wouldn't have been able to keep anything together. Jenny asked me a couple of times why I was being so quiet. I lamely said something about how the party had done me in.

The next day I finally caught sight of Nette. She was walking with Angelica by the shops. Jenny said hello and Angelica told us how they'd hired a car to travel up to a resort on the north coast. Nette and I hung quietly beside our respective girlfriends like two children being picked up from school whose mothers are chatting away between themselves. I tried to catch her eye but she was either looking down or at Jenny. We then wandered off in separate directions.

The day came for us to return to London. Jenny and I had a final swim in the sea and then a shower and afterwards threw our beach towels in the bin since they wouldn't be dry in time to pack. The taxi arrived and the cases were loaded into the boot. Mandy and Stella came to see us off, along with Monica and Danielle. Elena had already left the island and Debs and Susan were still at the resort but nowhere to be seen, even though we'd made sure to tell them what time we were going.

We all kissed and hugged goodbye and then I sat in the back seat, but Jenny said she had to nip to the cashpoint. Nette wouldn't have known what time I was leaving, but I was still hoping against hope that somehow she might miraculously turn up. The others were all chatting away by the roadside and I was alone in the car feeling sick to my stomach. All that I wanted to do with every part of my being was to go and find Nette, hold her and never let her go. So what was stopping me? Why was I going along with this charade? I knew that I must stay in the taxi, that this was the life I had chosen, this was what I wanted, wasn't it? But still I could feel my stomach clenching into a painful knot and my head spinning with confusion.

"Come on, Jenny," I was thinking. "Let's just get the hell out of here." But she didn't appear. And then out of nowhere I saw Nette. She was making her way towards the taxi with Angelica following and shouting something at her. Angelica tried to grab Nette's arm to hold her back, but Nette pulled away and ran up to the car. I was still sitting in the back seat with the window open and before I knew it she leant over and kissed me. Angelica came up right behind her, pulled her away from the car and shouted something in Dutch. All the other women around were dumbstruck – except Monica, who came straight over and, with a fiery look in her eyes, said, "What the hell's going on?"

Nette started calling out to me: "We can be together, you know we can make it work. You don't have to go away, stay with me."

At this point, Jenny returned and quickly took in the situation. She said to Angelica: "Take her away, NOW!" And Angelica frog-marched Nette from the scene. I could see that Nette's rage had turned to sorrow and she was sobbing as she was being dragged away. It was more than I could bear to watch and I jumped out of the taxi to run to her, but Jenny held me back and gently said: "Come on, darling, we have to go home."

She helped me back into the taxi and I sat there like someone who had been arrested and forced into a police car. But this was not against my will, I was doing it voluntarily. I was choosing to leave the only woman I wanted in the world right now, for Jenny, who at this point felt like a complete stranger to me. I realised that I hadn't even got a phone number for Nette. If I left her now, I could never change my mind. It seemed like the hardest decision I'd ever had to make. My head was aching with confusion and lust in equal measure and it felt like a drug had been released into my brain that I was powerless to resist with the inferior weapons of logic and willpower.

Nette and Angelica were almost out of sight now, and as they turned a street that took them out of my view, I knew that it was now or never, I had to make my choice.

My eyes filled up with tears and my stomach turned over once again as the taxi pulled away from the square. I felt physically sick with pain and longing, yet I stayed put in that car as it began the long, windy, mountainous journey across the island to the airport, to a flight back to England and my home with my girlfriend and all the remaining years of my life that I would spend without seeing Nette ever again.

## WHAT LESBIANS DO IN BED

As lesbians we live in a nation that is absolutely fascinated with our sex life. Straight people are always asking each other: "What do lesbians do? Do you know, in bed? What do they actually do?" Sometimes I think that the whole of Channel Five seems devoted to this particular quest for knowledge.

I want to make a programme for telly about what lesbians really do in bed and that way the public wouldn't need to guess any longer, it would all become crystal clear. I've worked it all out in my head, frame by frame... It would be aired after the watershed, of course, and it would start off with some soft and steamy introductory music, and then we'd catch our first glimpse of the Sapphic sex kittens in bed. There they'd be, Pat and Pauline from Peterborough. They're wearing matching jim-jams (M&S, tartan, 100% cotton). Pat's doing the crossword (the quick one, not the cryptic) with her vari-focals gently resting on the end of her nose. Pauline's resetting the radio from Two to Four, muttering, "Somebody keeps moving this dial around, Pat, and it certainly isn't me!" She wants to listen to *Book at Bedtime*. She's been following *Little House on the Prairie* all week. On Monday she hadn't thought that an adaptation would work on the radio, but it's Friday now and she's definitely changed her mind on that one.

At this point a soft-focus lens zooms in on Pat. Her look is slightly strained, her brow is furrowed. She quietly groans before asking: "What's an anagram of 'ice rot'? Six letters beginning in 'e'?" Pauline doesn't know, or doesn't care. She's immersed in prairie life and is worried about Laura's appointment with the optician. There's a serious possibility that the brave little girl might lose her sight completely.

The music crescendoes and there is now a wide shot encompassing the whole bed. We can see the outlines of two bodies, lying neatly beneath the duvet cover. Like a medieval burial tomb in a cathedral. And just as lively.

*Book at Bedtime* finishes on a cliffhanger. Not a metaphorical one; the father is quite literally dangling from a rock face, having been chased by a bear. Pat drops her paper onto the floor and, in a gliding motion that resembles two synchronised swimmers, the two women turn to face each other. They smile. They are both thinking the same thing. Tomorrow is Saturday. They are in no hurry to go to sleep.

The soundtrack quickens apace. The women's breathing becomes noticeably faster. They are about to indulge in their favourite activity. The thing they enjoy most after a hard week's work. Something that really binds them together as a couple. The camera moves in to a headshot of Pauline, then follows her hand, which reaches out to the bedside table. She grabs something that we cannot at first see and then brings it back into shot. It is a small tome. Pat produces a similar one from the cabinet on her side of the bed. The time has come for "Doing Diaries".

They start off with work commitments and move on to social engagements, scribbling away in unison. Then comes the fun bit. What will the weekend hold? Pat says she's going to have a bash at changing the plastic cutter on the strimmer but wouldn't mind some help if Pauline's free in the morning. Pauline says she really needs to settle down to an email session that isn't work-related. They both agree to go to Waitrose after lunch and if the weather holds to maybe have a barbeque the following evening and ask Mary and Monica if they fancy coming over.

I think it fair to say that, by this point, the eleven million viewers the programme's title has attracted will be completely glued to the telly. No one would dare take a tea- or pee-break at this crucial stage of proceedings. The nation is on tenterhooks... And finally it happens, what we've all been waiting for. Physical contact between the women. Pauline kisses Pat.

A sweet, soft, sensual, loving, but very-little-sign-of-tongues-after-all-this-time sort of kiss, on the cheek.

Pat reaches for the light switch but the wonders of fluorescent technology allow us to carry on seeing the two women in the dark.

They have moved a little closer to each other and are now in that well-known lesbian position called "Spoons". One body snuggling up, papoose-like, behind the other.

Pauline is heard to say, "Night night, darling." Pat is heard to say, "Night night, darling." Pauline is heard to say, "Good night, Baby Baalamb." Pauline may be the older of the two, but she still sleeps every night with her slightly scruffy but totally adorable stuffed sheep. Pat is heard to say, "Good night, Baby Baalamb." She doesn't really do the cuddly toy thing herself, but knows that it always brings a smile to Pauline's face if she joins in. The camera shot swirls upwards to the ceiling. The music crescendoes. The credits roll. The programme ends. And finally, finally, the public is enlightened. They now know exactly what it is that lesbians do in bed.

## WHY CAN'T I FIND SOMEONE NORMAL?

Why can't I find someone normal?
My lovers are always so strange.
I can't understand my attraction
For dykes who are clearly deranged.

I've a gift of spotting trouble at a hundred yards
And I know that a relationship is on the cards –
All the sensible advice from friends I'll disregard somehow.
I won't believe the lies about their exploitations,
Exaggerated stories of inebriation –
She says she's only violent in retaliation now.

Why can't I find someone single?
Believe me, each time that I try,
I find that they're already taken,
Which makes me a bit on the side.

My lover said she's single but I know she's lying,
I've done a little research – you could call it spying –
She's living with her girlfriend but it's not quite time to quit.
I'll tell her that she's better off by choosing me
But she says she "only sees me as a fantasy,
It would never really work as a reality". Bullshit!

Why are my lovers so jealous?
They think that I'm having affairs
With all of my friends and my exes –
Well, perhaps it just shows that they care.

When we go out on a date, my girlfriend's so possessive –
She'd really like me on a lead but that's excessive.
She'll drink too much and it's not an impressive sight.
I wouldn't say she's crazy but it has been known
For her to leave a message on my answerphone
Telling me she'll kill me if I don't come home that night!

Why can't I find someone normal?
I don't want to end up alone
But as long as I'm solving her problems...
I don't have to look at my own.

# ABOUT THE AUTHOR

**Clare Summerskill** is a writer, actress, stand-up and musician. She performs her one-woman shows at theatres around the UK. They include *Clare Summerskill Acts Her Age, The Bootleg Clare Summerskill* and *Fantasy Heckler.* Her theatre company, Artemis, toured nationally with *Gateway To Heaven,* a play based on the memories of older lesbians and gay men, which has since been made into a film by Age Concern England. Clare has written for sketch shows on BBC Radio 2 & 4 and appeared on *Richard & Judy* (Channel 4). She has also produced three albums of her songs, the latest being *Still Let Me Fly.*

Visit Clare's website: www.claresummerskill.co.uk

## *Music from Clare Summerskill*


### Make It Sound Easy

Clare's first album includes the tracks "Why Can't I Find
Someone Normal?" and "Obvious Dyke".

"Hugely enjoyable and delightfully versatile. Alternately witty
and moving, this totally original album contains a unique
mixture of catchy comedy numbers and beautiful love songs."
*Kenric*

## Feels Like Coming Home

The perfect present for your girlfriend, your girlfriend to be, your past girlfriend, your ex-girlfriend who is now your best friend… The possibilities are endless.

This CD includes favourites such as "Of Course I'll Tell My Mother that I'm Gay", "I'm a 'We'" and "I Still Dream of My History Teacher".

## Still Let Me Fly

Clare's latest album includes "Wedding Bells", "Therapy" and "We're the Girls".

"It's fantastic to have a CD entirely geared to lesbians with humour, love and politics. You'll laugh, cry and cheer!"
*Velvet*

**For details of how to order Clare's CDs, email: admin@claresummerskill.co.uk**